The Supporters' Guide to Premier & Football League Clubs 2020

EDITOR
Steve Askew

Thirty-sixth Edition

CONTENTS

British Library Cataloguing in Publication Data
A catalogue record for this book is available from the British Library

ISBN: 978-1-86223-406-2

72 St. Peter's Avenue, Cleethorpes, N.E. Lincolnshire, DN35 8HU, England
Web site www.soccer-books.co.uk
e-mail info@soccer-books.co.uk

Manufactured in the UK by Severn

FOREWORD

We are indebted to the staffs of all the clubs featured in this guide for their cooperation and also to Michael Robinson (page layouts), Bob Budd (cover artwork) and Tony Brown (Cup Statistics – www.soccerdata.com).

When using this guide, please note that concessions also include senior citizens unless stated otherwise. Some clubs had not fixed their matchday admission prices for 2019/2020 at the time of going to press and in these cases we have been unable to include current admission information. It should be noted that although actual matchday admission prices are shown in this guide, prices can vary and although many clubs offer discounts for tickets purchased before the day of the game, some prices may be higher than those stated. There is also a move towards variable 'demand-based' pricing at certain clubs.

Disabled Supporters' information is once again included in the guide and, to ensure that facilities are not overstretched, we recommend that fans with disabilities pre-book wherever possible.

Regular purchasers of the guide will notice that we have included a number of new ground photographs in this edition. Ground redevelopment is continuing apace and travelling fans may find that away sections and prices change during the course of the 2019/2020 season.

If any readers have alternative ground photos which they would like us to consider for insertion in future issues, they should write to me care of the address opposite.

Finally, we would like to wish our readers a happy and safe spectating season.

Steve Askew
EDITOR

WEMBLEY STADIUM

First Opened: 1923 (Re-opened in 2007 after rebuild)
Address: Wembley National Stadium, Wembley, London HA9 0WS
Correspondence: P.O.Box 1966, London, SW1P 3EQ
Telephone Nº: 0844 980-8001 or 0800 169-2007
Fax Number: (020) 8795-5050
Stadium Tours: 0800 169-9933

Seating Capacity: 90,000 over three tiers –
Lower Tier: 34,303 seats
Middle Tier: 16,532 seats
Upper Tier: 39,165 seats
Modern Era Record Attendance: 89,874 (2008)
Pitch Size: 115 × 75 yards
Web site: www.wembleystadium.com

GENERAL INFORMATION

Car Parking: The stadium is a Public Transport Location and, as such, parking is only available for pre-accredited vehicles. Any spaces which are available must be pre-purchased from the following web site: www.wembleyofficialparking.com
Coach Travel: National Express operates coach routes from hundreds of towns and cities direct to the stadium for special events: www.nationalexpress.com/wembley
Rail & Tube Travel: Wembley Park station is on the Jubilee and Metropolitan tube lines; Wembley Stadium station is on the Chiltern mainline and Wembley Central station is served by the Bakerloo tube, London Overground and London Midland and Southern railway lines.
Local Bus Services: Services 83, 92 and 224 all travel to the stadium

FANS WITH DISABILITIES INFORMATION

Wheelchairs: 310 spaces for wheelchairs are available in total alongside 310 seats for helpers. A further 100 enhanced amenity seats are available for ambulant visitors. 26 lifts around the stadium assist with access.
Disabled Toilets: 147 toilets are available throughout the stadium with access via the Radar Key system.
Contact: For information and assistance contact the Disability liaison officer on 0800 169-2007 (Option 7) or E-mail pod@wembleystadium.com

ACCRINGTON STANLEY FC

Founded: 1876 (Reformed 1968)
Former Names: None
Nickname: 'Stanley' 'Reds'
Ground: Wham Stadium, Livingstone Road, Accrington, Lancashire BB5 5BX
Record Attendance: 4,386 (7th May 2016)
Pitch Size: 112 × 72 yards

Colours: Red shirts and shorts
Telephone Nº: (01254) 356950
Fax Number: (01254) 356951
Ground Capacity: 5,057
Seating Capacity: 2,000
Web site: www.accringtonstanley.co.uk
E-mail: info@accringtonstanley.co.uk

GENERAL INFORMATION

Car Parking: A limited number of spaces are available at the ground – pre-booking required with a £5.00 charge. Otherwise, street parking only.
Coach Parking: Livingstone Road near the Away entrance
Nearest Railway Station: Accrington (1 mile)
Nearest Bus Station: Accrington Town Centre (1 mile)
Club Shop: At the ground and through the club web site
Opening Times: Weekdays 9.30am – 5.00pm; Saturday matchdays 10.30am – 5.30pm
Telephone Nº. (01254) 356950

GROUND INFORMATION

Away Supporters' Entrances & Sections:
Signposted on matchdays

ADMISSION INFO (2019/2020 PRICES)

Adult Standing: £20.00
Adult Seating: £20.00
Senior Citizen Standing: £15.00
Senior Citizen Seating: £15.00
Ages 12-17 Standing/Seating: £10.00
Under-12s Standing/Seating: £5.00
Programme Price: £3.00

FANS WITH DISABILITIES INFORMATION

Wheelchairs: Specific areas around the ground
Helpers: Admitted
Prices: Normal prices are charged for disabled fans. One helper is admitted free with each disabled supporter.
Disabled Toilets: Available
Contact: (01254) 356950 Robert Houseman, Disabled Liaison Officer (Bookings are necessary)

Travelling Supporters' Information:
Routes: Take the M6 to the M65 signposted for Blackburn/Burnley. Exit at Junction 7 and follow the sign for Padiham. Turn right at first traffic lights then right at next. Follow Whalley Road towards Accrington, go through lights at the Greyhound Inn. Turn left into Livingstone Road, 500 yards past traffic lights (signposted Accrington Stanley). The ground is signposted from Junction 7 of the M65 – follow the brown signs with the white football.

AFC BOURNEMOUTH

Founded: 1899 (**Entered League**: 1923)
Former Names: Boscombe FC (1899-1923); Bournemouth & Boscombe Athletic FC (1923-1972)
Nickname: 'Cherries'
Ground: Vitality Stadium, Dean Court, Bournemouth, Dorset BH7 7AF
Ground Capacity: 11,329 (All seats)

Record Attendance: 11,772 (21st July 2013)
Pitch Size: 115 × 74 yards
Colours: Red & Black striped shirts with Black shorts
Telephone Nº & Ticket Office Nº: 0344 576-1910
Fax Number: (01202) 726373
Web Site: www.afcb.co.uk
E-mail: enquiries@afcb.co.uk

GENERAL INFORMATION

Car Parking: Car Park for 200 cars behind the ground and free parking is available at Harewood College (10 mins. walk)
Coach Parking: At the ground
Nearest Railway Station: Bournemouth Central (1½ miles)
Nearest Bus Stop: Holdenhurst Road, Bournemouth
Club Shop: At the ground
Opening Times: Monday to Friday 9.00am to 5.00pm, Saturday 9.30am to 4.00pm, Sunday 10.00am to 3.00pm and Saturday Matchdays 9.00am to kick-off + 30 minutes after the final whistle.
Telephone Nº: 0844 576 -1910

GROUND INFORMATION

Away Supporters' Entrances & Sections:
East Stand turnstiles 'F' 14-16 for East Stand accommodation

ADMISSION INFO (2019/2020 PRICES)

Adult Seating: £32.00 – £55.00
Child Seating: £6.00 – £18.00
Concessionary Seating: £19.00 – £40.00
Note: Family tickets are also available. In view of the limited capacity of Dean Court, most seats for 2019/2020 will be taken by season ticket holders.

FANS WITH DISABILITIES INFORMATION

Wheelchairs: Spaces available in all stands
Helpers: One carer admitted per fan with disabilities
Prices: £5.00 for those in wheelchairs.
Disabled Toilets: Available in Main, East and North Stands
Contact: 0344 576-1910 (Bookings are necessary)
E-mail Contact: disability@afcb.co.uk

Travelling Supporters' Information: Routes: From the North & East: Take the A338 into Bournemouth and turn left at 'Kings Park' turning. After the slip road go straight forward at the mini-roundabout into Kings Park Drive – a car park is 500 yards on the left and the ground is nearby; From the West: Head into Bournemouth and join the A338, take the slip road at the Springbourne Roundabout, signposted for Kings Park. Take the 3rd exit at the roundabout at the fire station, stay in the left-hand lane and turn left onto Holdenhurst Road. Go straight on at the traffic lights (the Queen's Park Pub should be on the right) and take the 3rd exit at the mini roundabout into Kings Park for the ground.

AFC WIMBLEDON

Founded: 2002 (**Entered League**: 2011)
Former Names: Originally formed as Wimbledon Old Centrals (1889-1905) who later became Wimbledon FC
Nickname: 'The Dons'
Ground: The Cherry Red Records Stadium – Jack Goodchild Way, 422A Kingston Road, Kingston-upon-Thames, Surrey KT1 3PB
Record Attendance: 4,870 (2016)

Pitch Size: 112 × 71 yards
Ground Capacity: 5,234
Seating Capacity: 2,265
Colours: Shirts and Shorts are Blue with Yellow trim
Telephone Nº: (020) 8547-3528
Fax Number: 0808 280-0816
Web site: www.afcwimbledon.co.uk
E-mail: info@afcwimbledon.co.uk

GENERAL INFORMATION

Car Parking: At the ground
Coach Parking: At the ground
Nearest Railway Station: Norbiton (1 mile)
Nearest Bus Station: Kingston
Club Shop: At the ground plus online sales
Opening Times: Thursday to Friday 10.00am to 4.00pm and Matchdays 11.00am to 2.45pm (for a 3.00pm kick-off) or 5.00pm to 7.30pm (for a 7.45pm kick-off)
Telephone Nº: (020) 8547-3528

GROUND INFORMATION

Away Supporters' Entrances & Sections:
Turnstiles 9 and 10 for the Rygas Stand terracing and the John Green End seating.

ADMISSION INFO (2019/2020 PRICES)

Adult Standing: £17.00 – £20.00
Adult Seating: £24.00 – £29.00
Concessionary Standing: £11.00 – £12.00
Concessionary Seating: £15.00 – £18.00
Under-18s Standing: £4.00 – £5.00
Under-18s Seating: £10.00 – £13.00
Programme Price: £3.00

FANS WITH DISABILITIES INFORMATION

Wheelchairs: Accommodated around the ground
Helpers: Admitted
Prices: Normal prices for fans with disabilities. Helpers free
Disabled Toilets: Available
Contact: (020) 8547-3528 (Bookings are necessary)

Travelling Supporters' Information:
Routes: Exit the M25 at Junction 10 and take the A3 to the New Malden/Worcester Park turn-off and turn into Malden Road (A2043). Follow Malden Road to the mini-roundabout and turn left into Kingston Road. Kingsmeadow is situated approximately 1 mile up the Kingston Road, on the left-hand side and is signposted from the mini-roundabout.

ARSENAL FC

Founded: 1886 (**Entered League**: 1893)
Former Names: Royal Arsenal (1886-1891) and Woolwich Arsenal (1891-1914)
Nickname: 'Gunners'
Ground: Emirates Stadium, Hornsey Road, London, N7 7AJ
Ground Capacity: 60,260 (All seats)
Pitch Size: 115 × 74 yards
Record Attendance: 60,161 (3rd November 2007)
Colours: Red shirts with White sleeves, White shorts
Telephone Nº: (020) 7619-5003
Ticket Office: (020) 7619-5000
Fax Number: (020) 7704-4001
Office Address: Highbury House, 75 Drayton Park, London N5 1BU
Web Site: www.arsenal.com
E-mail: ask@arsenal.co.uk

GENERAL INFORMATION

Car Parking: None
Coach Parking: Visit the web site for further details
Nearest Railway Station: Finsbury Park and Highbury & Islington
Nearest Tube Station: Arsenal (Piccadilly), Finsbury Park, Highbury & Islington and Holloway Road are all nearby
Club Shop: At the ground and at Finsbury Park Tube Station
Opening Times: Monday to Saturday 9.00am to 6.00pm; Sundays 10.00am to 4.00pm
Telephone Nº: (020) 7619-5000

GROUND INFORMATION

Away Supporters' Entrances & Sections:
Green quadrant – follow colour coding system at the ground

ADMISSION INFO (2019/2020 PRICES)

Adult Seating: £26.00 – £95.50
Child Seating: £10.00 – £32.50 (Members only)
Senior Citizen Seating: £11.25 – £36.50 (Members only)
Note: Prices vary depending on the category of the game. Concessionary prices are only available to Members.
Programme Price: £3.00

FANS WITH DISABILITIES INFORMATION

Wheelchairs: 250 spaces available in areas throughout the ground. A similar number of places are available for the ambulant and visually impaired
Helpers: One helper admitted for each fan with disabilities
Prices: Registered supporters with disabilities are admitted for half the normal prices. Helpers are admitted free
Disabled Toilets: Many available throughout the ground
Free commentaries are available for the visually impaired
Contact: (020) 7619-5050 (Bookings are necessary)

Travelling Supporters' Information:
As the stadium is situated in a mainly residential area, only car owners with resident's permits will be allowed to park in the designated on-street parking areas. Cars parked illegally will be towed away so use public transport whenever possible. The nearest tube station is Arsenal (Piccadilly Line) which is 3 minutes walk from the ground with Finsbury Park (Victoria & Piccadilly Lines) and Highbury & Islington about 10 minutes walk away.

ASTON VILLA FC

Photo courtesy of Neville Williams/Aston Villa FC

Founded: 1874 (**Entered League**: 1888)
Former Names: None
Nicknames: 'The Villans' 'Villa'
Ground: Villa Park, Trinity Road, Birmingham B6 6HE
Ground Capacity: 42,785 (All seats)
Record Attendance: 76,588 (2nd March 1946)
Pitch Size: 115 × 75 yards

Colours: Claret shirts with Blue sleeves, White shorts
Telephone Nº: (0121) 327-2299
Fax Number: (0121) 322-2107
Ticket Office: 0333 323-1874
Consumer Sales: 0330 053-6010
Web Site: www.avfc.co.uk
E-mail: postmaster@avfc.co.uk

GENERAL INFORMATION

Ground Tours: 0333 323-1874
Car Parking: Please check the web site for information.
Away Coach Parking: Opposite the ground on Witton Lane
Nearest Railway Station: Witton or Aston (5 mins. walk)
Nearest Bus Station: Birmingham Centre
Club Shop: 'Villa Village' at the ground
Opening Times: Villa Village: Monday to Saturday 10.00am to 5.00pm (9.00am on Saturday) & Sunday 10.00am to 4.00pm.
Telephone Nº: 0330 053-6010

GROUND INFORMATION

Away Supporters' Entrances & Sections:
Doug Ellis Stand – Blocks 'P' & 'Q'

ADMISSION INFO (2019/2020 PRICES)

Adult Seating: £20.00 – £33.00
Concessionary Seating: £15.00 – £20.00
Under-21s Seating: £10.00 – £17.00
Under-16s Seating: £5.00 – £10.00
Programme Price: £3.50

FANS WITH DISABILITIES INFORMATION

Wheelchairs: 84 spaces in total in the Trinity Road Stand lower, 8 of which are for away supporters
Helpers: Admitted on request – one per fan with disabilities
Prices: Concessionary prices for fans with disabilities
Disabled Toilets: Available in the Trinity Road Stand lower
Contact: 0800 612-0970 ext. 344 (Bookings are necessary)
E-mail contact: disability@avfc.co.uk

Travelling Supporters' Information: From all parts: Exit M6 at Junction 6 (Spaghetti Junction). Follow signs for Birmingham (NE). Take the 4th exit at the roundabout onto the A38 (M) signposted Aston. After ½ mile, turn right into Aston Hall Road.
Bus Services: Service 7 from Colmore Circus to Witton Square. Also some specials.

BARNSLEY FC

Founded: 1887 (**Entered League**: 1898)
Former Names: Barnsley St. Peter's
Nickname: 'Reds'
Ground: Oakwell Stadium, Barnsley S71 1ET
Ground Capacity: 23,287 (All seats)
Record Attendance: 40,255 (15th February 1936)
Pitch Size: 110 × 75 yards

Colours: Red shirts with White shorts and Red socks
Telephone Nº: (01226) 211211
Ticket Office: (01226) 211183
Fax Number: (01226) 211444
Web Site: www.barnsleyfc.co.uk
E-mail: thereds@barnsleyfc.co.uk

GENERAL INFORMATION

Car Parking: Queen's Ground Car Park (adjacent)
Coach Parking: Queen's Ground Car Park
Nearest Railway Station: Barnsley Interchange (6 minutes walk)
Nearest Bus Station: Barnsley Interchange
Club Shop: At the Stadium
Opening Times: Monday to Friday 9.00am to 5.00pm. Saturdays 9.00am to 12.00pm. Saturday Matchdays open 9.00am to 3.00pm then 4.45pm to 5.15pm. Evening matchdays open 9.00am to 7.45pm
Telephone Nº: (01226) 211400

GROUND INFORMATION

Away Supporters' Entrances & Sections:
Palmer Construction North Stand Turnstiles 42-51

ADMISSION INFO (2019/2020 PRICES)

Adult Seating: £23.00 – £36.00
Concessionary Seating: £16.00 – £28.00
Under-19s Seating: £10.00
Under-12s Seating: £5.00
Note: Prices are lower for tickets purchased in advance
Programme Price: £3.00

FANS WITH DISABILITIES INFORMATION

Wheelchairs: 60 wheelchair spaces available in total in designated disabled areas including 18 spaces for Away fans in the North Stand.
Helpers: Admitted depending on room available
Prices: Normal prices for fans with disabilities but helpers are admitted free of charge
Disabled Toilets: Available in the Corner Stand, North Stand and C.K. Beckett Stand
Commentaries are available for the blind
Contact: (01266) 211183 (Bookings are necessary)

Travelling Supporters' Information: From All Parts: Exit the M1 at Junction 37 and follow the 'Barnsley FC/Football Ground' signs which lead to a large surface car park adjacent to the stadium (2 miles).

BIRMINGHAM CITY FC

Founded: 1875 (**Entered League**: 1892)
Former Names: Small Heath Alliance FC (1875-88); Small Heath FC (1888-1905); Birmingham FC (1905-45)
Nickname: 'The Blues'
Ground: St. Andrew's Trillion Trophy Stadium, Birmingham B9 4RL
Ground Capacity: 29,409 (All seats)
Record Attendance: 68,844 (11th March 1939)

Pitch Size: 109 × 74 yards
Colours: Royal Blue Shirts with White Shorts
Telephone Nº: (0121) 772-0101
Ticket Office: (0121) 772-0101 (Option 2)
Web Site: www.bcfc.com
E-mail: reception@bcfc.com

GENERAL INFORMATION

Car Parking: Street Parking + Birmingham Wheels (secure parking but not related to the club)
Coach Parking: Coventry Road
Nearest Railway Station: Birmingham New Street or Birmingham Moor Street (20 minutes walk)
Nearest Bus Station: Digbeth National Express Coach Station
Club Shops: Blues Store at the ground
Opening Times: Monday to Saturday 9.00am to 5.00pm. Matchdays open from 9.00am until kick-off then for a further 30 minutes after the game. Sundays 10.30am to 4.30pm.
Telephone Nº. (0121) 772-0101 (Option 4)

GROUND INFORMATION

Away Supporters' Entrances & Sections: Gil Merrick Stand, Coventry Road

ADMISSION INFO (2019/2020 PRICES)

Adult Seating: £15.00 – £35.00
Under-19s Seating: £10.00 – £25.00
Under-13s Seating: £5.00 – £20.00
Concessionary Seating: £10.00 – £30.00
Note: Prices vary depending on the category of the match and the location of the seat.

FANS WITH DISABILITIES INFORMATION

Wheelchairs: 88 spaces in total (including 21 for Away fans) in the Spion Kop Stand, Gil Merrick Lower Stand, Tilton Road Stand and East Paddocks
Helpers: One assistant admitted for each fan with disabilities
Prices: Normal prices apply for fans with disabilities. Helpers are admitted free of charge
Disabled Toilets: Available in the Spion Kop Stand, Family Stand, Gil Merrick Stand and Tilton Road Stand
Contact: (0121) 772-0101 Option 2 (Bookings are necessary)

Travelling Supporters' Information: From All Parts: Exit M6 at Junction 6 and take the A38 (M) (Aston Expressway). Leave at 2nd exit then take first exit at roundabout along the Dartmouth Middleway. After 1¼ miles turn left on to Coventry Road.
Bus Services: Services 17, 58, 59 & 60 from Birmingham Centre stop at Cattell Road just to the south of the stadium and Services 97f stops at Garrison Lane just to the north of the stadium.

BLACKBURN ROVERS FC

Founded: 1875 (**Entered League**: 1888)
Nickname: 'Rovers' 'Blues & Whites'
Ground: Ewood Park, Blackburn, Lancashire BB2 4JF
Pitch Size: 115 × 72 yards
Ground Capacity: 31,367 (All seats)
Record Attendance: 62,255 vs Bolton (2/3/1929)

Colours: Blue and White halved shirts, White shorts
Telephone Nº: (01254) 372001
Ticket Office: (01254) 372000
Fax Number: (01254) 671042
Web Site: www.rovers.co.uk
Contact E-mail: enquiries@rovers.co.uk

GENERAL INFORMATION

Car Parking: 800 spaces available at the ground
Coach Parking: At the ground (Darwen End)
Nearest Railway Station: Blackburn Central (1½ miles)
Nearest Bus Station: Blackburn Central (1½ miles)
Club Shop: Roverstore at the ground
Opening Times: Weekdays 9.00am – 5.00pm, Saturday 10.00am–3.00pm, closed on Sundays.
Telephone Nº: (01254) 508137 (Ewood shop)

GROUND INFORMATION

Away Supporters' Entrances & Sections:
Darwen End

ADMISSION INFO (2019/2020 PRICES)

Adult Seating: £22.00 – £45.00
Senior Citizen Seating: £15.00 – £35.00
Under-26s Seating: £10.00 – £30.00
Under-18s Seating: £7.00 – £16.00
Under-12s Seating: £5.00 – £14.00
Programme Price: £3.00

FANS WITH DISABILITIES INFORMATION

Wheelchairs: 262 spaces for Home fans and 30 for Away fans
Helpers: One helper admitted per fan with disabilities. Applications for helpers tickets must be made in advance
Prices: Normal prices apply for both fans with disabilities and their helpers
Disabled Toilets: 14 purpose-built ground level toilets
Commentaries available via Radio Rovers – bring a radio!
Contact: 0771 772-4646 **E-mail**: disability@rovers.co.uk

Travelling Supporters' Information: Routes: Supporters travelling Northbound on the M6: Exit the M6 at Junction 29, follow the M65 and exit at Junction 4 for Ewood Park. The ground is ¾ mile from Junction 4 – please look for parking areas to avoid congestion around the ground; Supporters travelling Northbound on the M61: Exit the M61 at Junction 9, join the M65 and exit at Junction 4 (then as above); Supporters travelling Southbound on the M6: Exit the M6 at Junction 30, follow the M61 and exit at Junction 9 onto the M65. Exit the M65 at Junction 4 for the ground; Supporters from the Yorkshire Area either on the B6234, the A56 Haslingden by-pass or the A59 Skipton Road – please follow signs for Ewood Park (follow Preston M65 and exit at Junction 4).

BLACKPOOL FC

Founded: 1887 (**Entered League**: 1896)
Former Name: Merged with Blackpool St.Johns (1887)
Nickname: 'Seasiders' or 'Tangerines'
Ground: Bloomfield Road, Blackpool, FY1 6JJ
Ground Capacity: 16,616 (All seats)
Record Attendance: 38,098 (17th September 1955)
Pitch Size: 112 × 75 yards

Colours: Tangerine shirts with White shorts
Telephone Nº: (01253) 599344
Ticket Office: (01253) 599745
Web Site: www.blackpoolfc.co.uk
E-mail: tickets@blackpoolfc.co.uk

GENERAL INFORMATION

Car Parking: 3,000 spaces at the ground and street parking
Coach Parking: Available at the ground
Nearest Railway Station: Blackpool South (5 mins. walk)
Nearest Bus Station: Talbot Road (2 miles)
Club Shop: At the ground
Opening Times: Daily from 9.00am to 5.30pm
Telephone Nº: (01253) 599745

GROUND INFORMATION

Away Supporters' Entrances & Sections:
North Side entrances for the East Stand (temporary)

ADMISSION INFO (2019/2020 PRICES)

Adult Seating: £20.00 – £28.00
Under-16s Seating: £10.00
Senior Citizen/Age 17 to 21 Seating: £18.00
Note: Under-5s are admitted free of charge
Programme Price: £3.00

FANS WITH DISABILITIES INFORMATION

Wheelchairs: Over 50 spaces in total for home and away fans
Helpers: One helper admitted with each fan with disabilities
Prices: Normal prices apply
Disabled Toilets: Available
Contact: 07875 236576 (Bookings are necessary)

Travelling Supporters' Information: From All Parts: Exit M6 at Junction 32 onto the M55. Follow signs for the main car parks along the new 'spine' road to the car parks at the side of the ground.

BOLTON WANDERERS FC

Founded: 1874 (**Entered League**: 1888)
Former Names: Christchurch FC (1874-1877)
Nickname: 'Trotters'
Ground: University of Bolton Stadium, Burnden Way, Lostock, Bolton, Lancashire BL6 6JW
Ground Capacity: 28,723 (All seats)
Pitch Size: 115 × 75 yards

Record Attendance: 28,353 (vs Leicester City, 2003)
Colours: White shirts with Navy Blue shorts
Telephone Nº: (01204) 673673
Ticket Office: 0844 871-2932
Fax Number: (01204) 673773
Web Site: www.bwfc.co.uk
E-mail: reception@bwfc.co.uk

GENERAL INFORMATION

Car Parking: 2,800 spaces available at the ground
Coach Parking: Available at the ground
Nearest Railway Station: Horwich Parkway (600 yards)
Nearest Bus Station: Moor Lane, Bolton
Club Shop: At the ground
Opening Times: Daily from 9.30am to 5.30pm
Telephone Nº: (01204) 673650

GROUND INFORMATION

Away Supporters' Entrances & Sections:
South Stand entrances and accommodation

ADMISSION INFO (2018/2019 PRICES)

Adult Seating: £15.00 – £35.00
Concessionary Seating: £10.00 – £29.00
Under-18s Seating: £10.00 – £12.00
Under-12s Seating: £10.00
Note: Prices vary depending on the grading of the game. Prices for the 2019/2020 season were not available at the time of going to press. Please contact the club for information.

FANS WITH DISABILITIES INFORMATION

Wheelchairs: 32 spaces available for visiting fans, 72 spaces for home fans
Helpers: One helper admitted free with each disabled fan
Prices: Normal prices apply for fans with disabilities
Disabled Toilets: Available
Contact: 0844 871-2932 (Bookings are necessary)

Travelling Supporters' Information:
From All Parts: Exit the M61 at Junction 6 and the ground is clearly visible ¼ mile away.

BRADFORD CITY FC

Founded: 1903 (**Entered League**: 1903)
Nickname: 'Bantams'
Ground: Northern Commercials Stadium at Valley Parade, Bradford BD8 7DY
Ground Capacity: 25,136 (All seats)
Record Attendance: 39,146 (11th March 1911)
Pitch Size: 113 × 70 yards

Colours: Claret and Amber Striped shirts with Black shorts and socks
Telephone Nº: (01274) 773355
Ticket Office: (01274) 770012
Fax Number: (01274) 773356
Web Site: www.bradfordcityfc.co.uk
E-mail: support@bradfordcityfc.co.uk

GENERAL INFORMATION

Car Parking: Street Parking and Car Parks (£3.00 charge)
Coach Parking: By Police direction
Nearest Railway Station: Bradford Foster Square
Nearest Bus Station: Bradford Interchange (1 mile)
Club Shop: At the ground
Opening Times: Monday to Friday 9.30am to 5.00pm and Saturday 10.00am to 3.00pm
Telephone Nº: (01274) 309945
Shop Web Site: www.bantams.clubstore.co.uk

GROUND INFORMATION

Away Supporters' Entrances & Sections:
T.L. Dallas Stand (South Stand)

ADMISSION INFO (2019/2020 PRICES)

Adult Seating: £25.00 (£20.00 purchased in advance)
Under-16s Seating: £10.00
Senior Citizen/Student Seating: £15.00
Note: Under-11s are admitted for £5.00 when accompanied by a paying adult – up to 3 Under-11s admitted per adult.
Programme Price: £3.00

FANS WITH DISABILITIES INFORMATION

Wheelchairs: 100 spaces available in total for Home and Away fans throughout the ground. Access for away supporters is in the South Stand
Helpers: One helper admitted per fan with disabilities
Prices: Normal prices for fans with disabilities. Helpers free
Disabled Toilets: Available
Contact: 0871 978-8000 (Bookings are necessary)

Travelling Supporters' Information: Routes: Exit the M62 at Junction 26 and take the M606 towards Bradford. At the end of the motorway get in the middle lane and follow signs for Bradford (West) into Rooley Lane (signs for the Airport). A McDonalds is now on your left. Turn left into Wakefield Road at the roundabout and stay in the middle lane. Continue straight on over two roundabouts (signs to Shipley and Skipton) onto Shipley Airedale Road which then becomes Canal Road. Just after Tesco on the left, turn left into Station Road and left again into Queens Road. Go up the hill to the third set of traffic lights and turn left into Manningham Lane. After the Gulf petrol station on the left, turn first left into Valley Parade for the Stadium.

BRENTFORD FC

Photo courtesy of Mark Chapman

Founded: 1889 (**Entered League**: 1920)
Nickname: 'The Bees'
Ground: Griffin Park, Braemar Road, Brentford, Middlesex TW8 0NT
Ground Capacity: 12,763
Seating Capacity: 8,949
Record Attendance: 38,678 (26th February 1949)

Pitch Size: 110 × 74 yards
Colours: Red & White striped shirts with Black shorts
Telephone Nº: (020) 8847-2511
Ticket Office: 0333 005-8521
Fax Number: (020) 8568-9940
Web Site: www.brentfordfc.com
E-mail: enquiries@brentfordfc.com

GENERAL INFORMATION

Car Parking: Street Parking
Coach Parking: By Police direction
Nearest Railway Station: Brentford (½ mile)
Nearest Tube Station: South Ealing (Piccadilly) (1 mile)
Club Shop: Adjacent to the ground in Braemar Road
Opening Times: Weekdays 10.00am–4.00pm and Saturday Matchdays 12.00pm until kick-off and then for one hour after the game.
Telephone Nº: (020) 8847-2511 Option 4

GROUND INFORMATION

Away Supporters' Entrances & Sections:
Brook Road Upper and Lower for both seating and terracing

ADMISSION INFO (2019/2020 PRICES)

Adult Standing: £23.00 – £25.00
Adult Seating: £23.00 – £30.00
Under-18s Standing/Seating: £6.00 – £8.00
Senior Citizen Standing: £17.00 – £19.00
Senior Citizen Seating: £17.00 – £24.00
Ages 18 to 24 Standing: £15.00 – £17.00
Ages 18 to 24 Seating: £15.00 – £22.00
Programme Price: £3.00

FANS WITH DISABILITIES INFORMATION

Wheelchairs: 10 spaces for Home fans, 2 spaces for Away fans in a special section in the Braemar Road Stand
Helpers: One helper admitted per fan with disabilities
Prices: Normal prices for fans with disabilities. Helpers free
Disabled Toilets: Available in the Braemar Road Stand
Commentaries are available for the blind
Contact: (020) 8847-2511 Option 0 (Bookings necessary)

Travelling Supporters' Information: Routes: From the North: Take the A406 North Circular (from the M1/A1) to the Chiswick Roundabout and then along the Great West Road and turn left at the third set of traffic lights into Ealing Road for the ground; From the East: Take the A406 to the Chiswick Roundabout, then as North; From the West: Exit M4 at Junction 2 – down to the Chiswick Roundabout, then as North; From the South: Use the A3, M3, A240 or A316 to Kew Road, continue along over Kew Bridge, turn left at the traffic lights, then right at the next traffic lights into Ealing Road.

BRIGHTON & HOVE ALBION FC

Founded: 1901 (**Entered League**: 1920)
Nickname: 'Seagulls'
Ground: American Express Community Stadium, Village Way, Brighton BN1 9BL
Ground Capacity: 30,666 (All seats)
Pitch Size: 115 × 75 yards
Record Attendance: 30,682 (vs Everton, 2019)

Colours: Blue & White striped shirts with Blue shorts
Telephone Nº: 0344 324-6282
Ticket Office: 0844 327-1901
Fax Number: (01273) 878238
Web Site: www.brightonandhovealbion.com
E-mail: supporter.services@bhafc.co.uk

GENERAL INFORMATION

Car Parking: Limited parking at the stadium and 700 spaces available at the University campus (adjacent)
Coach Parking: At the stadium
Nearest Railway Station: Falmer (adjacent)
Nearest Bus Station: Brighton
Club Shop: At the stadium
Opening Times: Monday to Saturday 9.30am to 5.00pm and Sundays 11.00am to 4.00pm. Saturday Matchdays open 9.00am to kick-off then after the game until either 6.00pm or 10.30pm, depending on kick-off time.
Telephone Nº: 0845 496-9442

GROUND INFORMATION

Away Supporters' Entrances & Sections:
South Stand

ADMISSION INFO (2019/2020 PRICES)

Adult Seating: £30.00 – £65.00
Under-18s Seating: £15.00 – £32.00
Under-21s/Senior Citizen Seating: £23.00 – £45.00
Note: Prices vary depending on the category of the game
Programme Price: £3.50

FANS WITH DISABILITIES INFORMATION

Wheelchairs: 185 spaces available in total
Helpers: One helper admitted per fan with disabilities
Prices: Normal prices for fans with disabilities. Helpers free
Disabled Toilets: Yes – in all the stands
Contact: 0344 324-6282 (Bookings are necessary)

Travelling Supporters' Information: Routes: From the North: Take the M23 then the A23 to Brighton. At the roundabout on the outskirts of Brighton, take the exit onto the A27 towards Lewes. Pass the A270 turn-off and continue towards the village of Falmer. The stadium is situated by the side of the A27 in the village of Falmer across the road from the University of Sussex campus; From the East and West: Take the A27 to Falmer which is located to the north-east of Brighton. Then as above.

BRISTOL CITY FC

Founded: 1894 (**Entered League**: 1901)
Former Name: Bristol South End FC (1894-1897)
Nickname: 'The Robins'
Ground: Ashton Gate Stadium, Bristol BS3 2EJ
Ground Capacity: 27,000 (All seats)
Pitch Size: 115 × 75 yards
Record Attendance: 43,335 (16th February 1935)

Colours: Red shirts with White shorts
Telephone Nº: (0117) 963-0600
Ticket Hotline: (0117) 963-0600 (Option 1)
Fax Number: (0117) 963-0700
Web Site: www.bcfc.co.uk
E-mail: supporterservices@bristol-sport.co.uk

GENERAL INFORMATION

Car Parking: Street parking and also at Bedminster Cricket Club (5 minutes walk)
Coach Parking: By prior arrangement with the club
Nearest Railway Station: Bristol Temple Meads (1½ miles)
Nearest Bus Station: Bristol City Centre
Club Shop: BCFC Megastore at the ground
Opening Times: Monday to Saturday 9.00am to 5.00pm and weekend matchdays from 5.00pm until half an hour after the final whistle.
Telephone Nº: (0117) 963-0600 (Option 0 then Option 1)

GROUND INFORMATION

Away Supporters' Entrances & Sections:
Atyeo Stand – Turnstiles 39-46 via Ashton Road

ADMISSION INFO (2019/2020 PRICES)

Adult Seating: £25.00 – £42.00
Under-25s/Senior Citizen Seating: £22.00 – £39.00
Under-22s Seating: £19.00 – £36.00
Under-19s Seating: £15.00 – £23.00
Under-12s Seating: £10.00 – £18.00
Note: A membership scheme offers discounted prices for advance bookings. Prices vary depending on game category
Programme Price: £3.00

FANS WITH DISABILITIES INFORMATION

Wheelchairs: 20 spaces are available for away fans
Helpers: One helper admitted per fan with disabilities
Prices: Normal prices for fans with disabilities. Helpers free
Disabled Toilets: Available in various areas of the ground
Commentaries are available for the blind
Contact: (0117) 963-0670 Gareth Torpey (Bookings are necessary)

Travelling Supporters' Information: Routes: From the North & West: Exit the M5 at Junction 16, take the A38 to Bristol City Centre and follow the A38 Taunton signs. Cross the swing bridge after 1¼ miles and bear left into Winterstoke Road for the ground; From the East: Take the M4 then M32 and follow signs for the City Centre. Then as for North and West; From the South: Exit the M5 at Junction 19 and follow Taunton signs over the swing bridge (then as above).
Away Fans Car Parking: Bedminster Cricket Club, Clanidge Road, Bristol – SatNav: BS3 2JX (½ mile from Ashton Gate)
Bus Services: Services 27A and 28A from Bristol Temple Meads Station. A bus leaves Temple Meads 1 hour prior to kick-off.

BRISTOL ROVERS FC

Founded: 1883 (**Re-entered League**: 2015)
Former Names: Black Arabs FC (1883-84);
Eastville Rovers FC (1884-96);
Bristol Eastville Rovers FC (1896-97)
Nickname: 'Pirates' 'Rovers' 'Gas'
Ground: Memorial Stadium, Filton Avenue, Horfield, Bristol BS7 0BF
Pitch Size: 110 × 71 yards

Ground Capacity: 11,000
Seating Capacity: 3,307
Record Attendance: 12,011 (9th March 2008)
Colours: Blue & White quartered shirts, White shorts
Telephone N°: (0117) 909-6648
Fax Number: (0117) 907-4312
Web Site: www.bristolrovers.co.uk

GENERAL INFORMATION

Car Parking: Very limited number of spaces at the ground and street parking
Coach Parking: At the ground
Nearest Railway Station: Temple Meads (2 miles)
Nearest Bus Station: Bristol City Centre
Club Shop: At the ground
Opening Times: Monday to Friday, 9.00am to 5.00pm. Open from 9.00am to 1.00pm on non-match Saturdays and 9.00am until kick-off then after the game on matchdays.
Telephone N°: (0117) 909-6648 Option 1

GROUND INFORMATION

Away Supporters' Entrances & Sections:
Entrance to East Terrace & South Stand via Filton Avenue

ADMISSION INFO (2019/2020 PRICES)

Adult Standing: £19.00 – £21.00
Adult Seating: £23.00 – £25.00
Under-21s/ Concessionary Standing: £15.00 – £17.00
Under-21s/Concessionary Seating: £19.00 – £21.00
Under-16s Standing: £10.00
Under-16s Seating: £10.00 – £12.00
Under-11s Standing: £5.00
Under-11s Seating: £5.00 – £7.00
Programme Price: £3.00

FANS WITH DISABILITIES INFORMATION

Wheelchairs: 25 spaces in total including 6 spaces for Away fans in front of the East Stand and West Stand
Helpers: One helper admitted per fan with disabilities
Prices: £7.00 to £12.00 (depending on age) for fans in wheelchairs and the ambulant. Helpers are admitted free
Disabled Toilets: Available in the East Stand and West Stand
Contact: (0117) 909-6648 Option 1 (Bookings are necessary)

Travelling Supporters' Information: Routes: From All Parts: Exit the M32 at Junction 2 then take the exit at the roundabout (signposted Horfield) into Muller Road. Continue for approximately 1½ miles passing straight across 3 sets of traffic lights. At the 6th set of traffic lights turn left into Filton Avenue and the ground is immediately on the left.

BURNLEY FC

Founded: 1882 (**Entered League**: 1888)
Former Name: Burnley Rovers FC
Nickname: 'Clarets'
Ground: Turf Moor, Harry Potts Way, Burnley, Lancashire BB10 4BX
Ground Capacity: 21,401 (All seats)
Record Attendance: 54,775 (23rd February 1924)

Pitch Size: 115 × 75 yards
Colours: Claret and Sky Blue shirts and shorts
Telephone N°: (01282) 446800
Ticket Office: 0844 807-1882
Fax Number: (01282) 700014
Web Site: www.burnleyfootballclub.com
E-mail: info@burnleyfc.com

GENERAL INFORMATION

Car Parking: Matchday parking restrictions in surrounding streets so it is recommended that the various Town Centre car parks are used by visiting fans.
Coach Parking: By Police direction
Nearest Railway Station: Burnley Central (1½ miles)
Nearest Bus Station: Burnley (5 minutes walk)
Club Shop: At the ground and at Charter Walk Shopping Centre, 4 Fleet Walk, Burnley BB11 1QE
Opening Times: At Turf Moor: Monday to Friday and non-match Saturdays 9.00am – 5.00pm; Saturday matchdays open from 9.00am to kick-off then for 1 hour after the game. At Charter Walk: Monday to Saturday 9.00am to 5.30pm and Sunday 10.00am – 4.00pm.
Telephone N°: (01282) 700016 or (01282) 453914

GROUND INFORMATION

Away Supporters' Entrances & Sections:
Ladbrokes Stand

ADMISSION INFO (2019/2020 PRICES)

Adult Seating: £30.00 – £40.00
Under-18s Seating: £15.00 – £20.00
Under-12s Seating: £10.00 (with a paying adult in the Family Stand only)
Under-22s/Senior Citizen Seating: £20.00 – £25.00
Programme Price: £3.00

FANS WITH DISABILITIES INFORMATION

Wheelchairs: 35 spaces available in the four designated wheelchair areas aroundd the ground.
Helpers: One helper admitted for each wheelchair user
Prices: Normal prices apply for fans with disabilities plus one helper admitted free of charge
Disabled Toilets: Available
Commentary radios are available to purchase for a nominal fee.
Contact: (01282) 446800 (Bookings are necessary)

Travelling Supporters' Information: Routes: From the North: Follow the A682 to the Town Centre and take first exit at roundabout (Gala Club) into Yorkshire Street. Follow through traffic signals into Harry Potts Way; From the East: Follow the A646 to the A671 then along Todmorden Road towards the Town Centre. At the traffic signals (crossroads) turn right into Harry Potts Way; From the West & South: Exit the M6 at Junction 29 onto the M65. Exit the M65 at Junction 10 and follow signs for Burnley Football Club. At the roundabout in the town centre take the third exit into Yorkshire Street. Then as from the North.

BURTON ALBION FC

Founded: 1950 (**Entered League**: 2009)
Former Names: None
Nickname: 'The Brewers'
Ground: The Pirelli Stadium, Princess Way, Burton-on-Trent DE13 0AR
Record Attendance: 6,746 (vs Derby County, 2016)
Pitch Size: 110 × 72 yards

Colours: Yellow shirts with Black trim, Black shorts
Telephone Nº: (01283) 565938
Fax Number: (01283) 523199
Ground Capacity: 6,912 **Seating Capacity**: 2,034
Web site: www.burtonalbionfc.co.uk
E-mail: bafc@burtonalbionfc.co.uk

GENERAL INFORMATION

Car Parking: 400 spaces available at the ground (£5.00)
Coach Parking: Available at Claymills Pumping Station, Meadow Lane, Burton-on-Trent DE13 0DA (approximately 1 mile). Stewards will direct if necessary.
Nearest Railway Station: Burton-on-Trent (1½ miles)
Nearest Bus Station: Burton-on-Trent (1½ miles)
Club Shop: At the ground
Opening Times: Weekdays 8.30am to 5.30pm and Matchdays from 9.00am until kick-off
Telephone Nº: (01283) 565938

GROUND INFORMATION

Away Supporters' Entrances & Sections:
East Stand, Derby Road

ADMISSION INFO (2019/2020 PRICES)

Adult Standing: £20.00 **Adult Seating**: £24.00
Under-17s Standing: £7.00 **Under-17s Seating**: £14.00
Ages 17 to 22 Standing: £15.00 **Seating**: £22.00
Senior Citizen Standing: £18.00 **Seating**: £22.00
Note: Cheaper 'Early bird' prices are available for tickets purchased before 5.00pm on the day before the game.
Programme Price: £3.00

FANS WITH DISABILITIES INFORMATION

Wheelchairs: Over 78 spaces available for home and away fans in designated areas (East Terrace for away fans).
Helpers: Admitted
Prices: Normal prices for fans with disabilities. Helpers free
Disabled Toilets: Available in all stands
Contact: (01283) 565938 (Bookings are necessary)

Travelling Supporters' Information:
Routes: From the M1, North and South: Exit at Junction 23A and join the A50 towards Derby (also signposted for Alton Towers). Join the A38 southbound at the Toyota factory (towards Burton & Lichfield) then exit for Burton North onto the A5121. Continue past the Pirelli factory on the right and the BP Garage and Cash & Carry on the left then turn into Princess Way at the roundabout; From the M5/6 South: Join the M42 northbound and exit onto the A446 signposted Lichfield. Follow signs for the A38 to Burton then exit onto A5121 as above; From the M6 North: Exit at Junction 15 and follow the A50 towards Stoke and Uttoxeter. Exit the A50 for the A38 southbound signposted Burton and Lichfield at the Toyota factory, then as above.
SatNav users should enter the following post code: DE13 0BH

BURY FC

Founded: 1885 (**Entered League**: 1894)
Nickname: 'Shakers'
Ground: The Energy Check Stadium at Gigg Lane, Bury, Lancashire BL9 9HR
Ground Capacity: 11,313 (All seats)
Pitch Size: 112 × 73 yards
Record Attendance: 35,000 (9th January 1960)

Colours: White shirts with Royal Blue shorts & socks
Telephone Nº: (0161) 764-4881
Ticket Office: (0161) 764-4881 Option 1
Web Site: www.buryfc.co.uk
E-mail: admin@buryfc.co.uk

GENERAL INFORMATION

Car Parking: Designated car parks only
Coach Parking: By Police direction
Nearest Railway Station: Bury Interchange (1 mile)
Nearest Bus Station: Bury Interchange
Club Shop: At the ground
Opening Times: Saturday matchdays 10.00am to 5.00pm.
Telephone Nº: (0161) 764-4881 Option 3

GROUND INFORMATION

Away Supporters' Entrances & Sections:
Gigg Lane entrance for the East Stand

ADMISSION INFO (2019/2020 PRICES)

Adult Seating: £20.00
Concessionary Seating: £14.00
Under-18s Seating: £10.00
Under-12s Seating: £5.00 (must be accompanied by a paying adult)
Under-5s Seating: Free of charge
Programme Price: £2.00

FANS WITH DISABILITIES INFORMATION

Wheelchairs: Spaces for 26 wheelchairs in home fans area and a further 25 spaces in the Away Supporters' Section
Helpers: One helper admitted per wheelchair
Prices: £14.00 for fans with disabilities. Free for helpers
Disabled Toilets: Available
A Radio Commentary is available in the Press Box for the Registered Blind
Contact: (0161) 764-4881 (Bookings are not necessary)

Travelling Supporters' Information: Routes: From the North: Exit the M66 at Junction 2, take Bury Road (A58) for ½ mile, then turn left into Heywood Street and follow this into Parkhills Road until its end, turn left into Manchester Road (A56) and then left again into Gigg Lane. From the South, East and West: Exit the M60 at Junction 17, take Bury Road (A56) for 3 miles and then turn right into Gigg Lane.

CAMBRIDGE UNITED FC

Founded: 1912 (**Re-entered League**: 2014)
Former Name: Abbey United FC (1912-1951)
Nickname: 'U's' 'United'
Ground: Abbey Stadium, Newmarket Road, Cambridge CB5 8LN
Ground Capacity: 8,127
Seating Capacity: 4,376
Pitch Size: 110 × 74 yards

Record Attendance: 14,000 (1st May 1970)
Colours: Amber and Black striped shirts, Black shorts
Telephone Nº: (01223) 566500
Ticket Office: (01223) 566500 (Option 1)
Fax Number: (01223) 729220
Web Site: www.cambridge-united.co.uk
E-mail: info@cambridge-united.co.uk

GENERAL INFORMATION

Car Parking: Street parking only
Coach Parking: Coldhams Road
Nearest Railway Station: Cambridge (2 miles)
Nearest Bus Station: Cambridge City Centre
Club Shop: At the ground
Opening Times: Monday to Friday 10.00am to 4.00pm and Matchdays 10.00am to kick-off
Telephone Nº: (01223) 566500 Option 2

GROUND INFORMATION

Away Supporters' Entrances & Sections:
Coldham Common turnstiles 20-22 – Habbin Terrace (South) and South Stand (Seating) turnstiles 23-26

ADMISSION INFO (2018/2019 PRICES)

Adult Standing: £18.00 **Seating**: £20.00 – £24.00
Junior Standing/Seating: £7.00
Under-18s Standing: £10.00 **Seating**: £10.00 – £20.00
Concessionary Standing: £14.00
Concessionary Seating: £15.00 – £20.00
Programme Price: £3.00
Note: Prices for the 2019/2020 season were not available at the time of going to press. Please contact the club for details.

FANS WITH DISABILITIES INFORMATION

Wheelchairs: 34 spaces for Home fans in sections in front of Main Stand and in the North Terrace. 10 spaces for Away fans in the South Stand.
Helpers: One helper admitted per fan with disabilities
Prices: Normal prices apply for the disabled. Free for helpers
Disabled Toilets: Available
Contact: (01223) 566500 (Early booking strongly advised)

Travelling Supporters' Information: From the North: Take the A14 from Huntingdon, then turn east along the A14 dual carriageway. Exit the A14 at the 4th junction (to the east of Cambridge), up the slip road signposted Stow-cum-Quy then turn right onto the A1303, returning westwards towards Cambridge. Go straight on at the first roundabout passing the Airport on the left then straight on at two sets of traffic lights. Go straight on at the next roundabout and the ground is on the left after 700 yards; From the South: Exit the M11 at Junction 14 and turn east along the A14 dual carriageway. Then as from the North.
Bus Services: Services from the Railway Station to the City Centre and Nº 3 from the City Centre to the Ground.

CARDIFF CITY FC

Founded: 1899 (**Entered League**: 1920)
Former Names: Riverside FC (1899-1902) and Riverside Albion FC (1902-1908)
Nickname: 'Bluebirds'
Ground: Cardiff City Stadium, Leckwith Road, Cardiff CF11 8AZ
Record Attendance: 33,028 (22nd December 2018)
Ground Capacity: 33,316 (All seats)

Pitch Size: 110 × 75 yards
Colours: Blue shirts and shorts
Telephone Nº: 0333 311-1927
Ticket Office: 0845 345-1400 or 0333 311-1920
Fax Number: 0845 365-1116
Web Site: www.cardiffcityfc.co.uk
E-mail: club@cardiffcityfc.co.uk

GENERAL INFORMATION

Car Parking: Stadium car park and Street Parking
Coach Parking: Stadium car park (adjacent)
Nearest Railway Station: Cardiff Central (1 mile) and also Ninian Park Station (500 yards)
Nearest Bus Station: Cardiff Central
Club Shop: At the ground
Opening Times: Weekdays from 9.00am to 5.00pm and Saturdays 10.00am to 4.00pm
Telephone Nº: 0333 311-1922
Postal Sales: Yes (Internet Sales also accepted)

GROUND INFORMATION

Away Supporters' Entrances & Sections:
Grange End, Gate 07 – sections 119 to 122

ADMISSION INFO (2019/2020 PRICES)

Adult Seating: £17.00 – £34.00
Concessionary Seating: £13.00 – £29.00
Ages 16 to 21 Seating: £10.00 – £24.00
Under-16s Seating: £7.00 – £19.00
Note: Prices vary depending on the classification of the game and cheaper prices are available in the Family area.

FANS WITH DISABILITIES INFORMATION

Wheelchairs: Numerous spaces available for fans with disabilities in various areas around the ground
Helpers: One helper admitted per fan with disabilities
Prices: Normal prices for fans with disabilities. Helpers admitted free of charge
Disabled Toilets: Available – access via Radar Key system
Contact: 0845 365-1115 (Away fans tickets are normally sold in advance but may be available on the day)

Travelling Supporters' Information:
Routes: From All Parts: Exit M4 at Junction 33 and follow Penarth (A4232) signs. After 6 miles, take the B4267 to Cardiff City Stadium.

CARLISLE UNITED FC

Founded: 1903 (**Entered League**: 1928)
Former Names: Formed with the amalgamation of Shaddongate United FC and Carlisle Red Rose FC
Nickname: 'Cumbrians' 'Blues'
Ground: Brunton Park Stadium, Warwick Road, Carlisle CA1 1LL
Ground Capacity: 17,949
Seating Capacity: 7,594

Record Attendance: 27,500 (5th January 1957)
Pitch Size: 112 × 74 yards
Colours: Royal Blue shirts and shorts
Telephone Nº: (01228) 526237
Ticket Office: 0844 371-1921
Fax Number: (01228) 554141
Web Site: www.carlisleunited.co.uk
E-mail: enquiries@carlisleunited.co.uk

GENERAL INFORMATION

Car Parking: Rear of Ground via St.Aidans Road (£3.00)
Coach Parking: St.Aidans Road Car Park
Nearest Railway Station: Carlisle Citadel (1 mile)
Nearest Bus Station: Lowther Street, Carlisle
Club Shop: At the ground
Opening Times: Monday to Friday 10.00am – 5.00pm (and until 7.45pm for evening matches). Saturday Matchdays open 10.00am to 5.30pm (but closes at 3.00pm on other Saturdays).
Telephone Nº: (01228) 554138

GROUND INFORMATION

Away Supporters' Entrances & Sections:
North End (Blocks 2 and 3) of the Pioneer Stand

ADMISSION INFO (2019/2020 PRICES)

Adult Standing: £16.00 – £19.00 **Seating**: £19 – £22
Ages 18-22 Standing: £10.00–£13.00 **Seating**: £13–£16
Ages 11-17 Standing: £7.00 **Seating**: £10.00
Under-11s Standing: £4.00 **Under-11s Seating**: £7.00
Under-7s: Admitted free of charge
Senior Citizen Standing: £13.00 – £16.00
Senior Citizen Seating: £16.00 – £19.00
Note: Tickets are cheaper if purchased before the matchday
Programme Price: £3.00

FANS WITH DISABILITIES INFORMATION

Wheelchairs: 23 spaces for wheelchairs in a special section.
Helpers: One helper admitted per fan with disabilities
Prices: Fans in wheelchairs are admitted for £4.00. Helpers are admitted free of charge.
Disabled Toilets: Available
Contact: (01228) 554168 Nigel Dickinson (Bookings are recommended). E-mail nigel.dickinson@carlisleunited.co.uk

Travelling Supporters' Information:
Routes: From the North, South and East: Exit the M6 at Junction 43 and follow signs for Carlisle (A69) into Warwick Road for the ground; From the West: Take the A69 straight into Warwick Road.

CHARLTON ATHLETIC FC

Founded: 1905 (**Entered League**: 1921)
Nickname: 'Addicks'
Ground: The Valley, Floyd Road, Charlton, London, SE7 8BL
Ground Capacity: 27,111 (All seats)
Record Attendance: 75,031 (12th February 1938)
Pitch Size: 111 × 73 yards

Colours: Red shirts with White shorts
Telephone Nº: (020) 8333-4000
Ticket Office: 03330 144444
Fax Number: (020) 8333-4001
Web Site: www.cafc.co.uk
E-mail: info@cafc.co.uk

GENERAL INFORMATION

Car Parking: Street Parking
Coach Parking: By Police direction
Nearest Railway Station: Charlton (2 minutes walk)
Nearest Bus Station: At Charlton Railway Station as above
Club Shop: At the ground
Opening Times: Weekdays 9.30am – 5.00pm, Saturday Matchdays10.00am until 30 minutes after the Final whistle, Weekday matches from 9.30am until 30 minutes after the Final whistle and Non-Match Saturdays 10.00am – 4.00pm
Telephone Nº: (020) 8333-4035

GROUND INFORMATION

Away Supporters' Entrances & Sections:
Valley Grove/Jimmy Seed Stand

ADMISSION INFO (2019/2020 PRICES)

Adult Seating: £21.00 – £31.00
Student Seating: £12.00 – £15.00
Senior Citizen/Under-21s Seating: £17.00 – £23.00
Under-18s Seating: £10.00
Under-11s Seating: £5.00
Programme Price: £3.00

FANS WITH DISABILITIES INFORMATION

Wheelchairs: 96 spaces available for Home fans in the West and East Stands. 7 spaces available for Away fans in the South (Jimmy Seed) Stand
Helpers: One helper admitted per fan with disabilities
Prices: Helpers are admitted free of charge. Fans in wheelchairs pay concessionary prices
Disabled Toilets: Available in West and East Stands
Commentaries are available – please ring for details
Contact: 03330 144444 (Ticket Office –Bookings are necessary) or the Disability Liaison Officer: (020) 8333-4000

Travelling Supporters' Information:
Routes: From All Parts: Exit the M25 at Junction 2 (A2 London-bound) and follow until the road becomes the A102(M). Take the exit marked Woolwich Ferry and turn right along the A206 Woolwich Road. After approximately 1 mile do a U-turn at the roundabout back along Woolwich Road. At the traffic lights turn left into Charlton Church Lane and Floyd Road is the 2nd left.

CHELSEA FC

Founded: 1905 (**Entered League**: 1905)
Nickname: 'Blues'
Ground: Stamford Bridge, Fulham Road, London, SW6 1HS
Ground Capacity: 41,631 (All seats)
Record Attendance: 82,905 (12th October 1935)
Pitch Size: 113 × 74 yards

Colours: Blue shirts and shorts
Telephone Nº: 0371 811-1955
+44 207 386-9373 (International callers)
Ticket Office: 0371 811-1905
+44 207 835-6000 (International callers)
Fax Number: (020) 7381-4831
Web Site: www.chelseafc.com

GENERAL INFORMATION

Car Parking: Pre-booked underground car park at ground
Coach Parking: By Police direction
Nearest Tube Station: Fulham Broadway (District)
Club Shop: Chelsea Megastore – at the ground
Opening Times: Monday to Saturday 9.00am – 6.00pm; Sundays 11.00am–5.00pm; Bank Holidays 11.00am – 5.00pm
Stadium tours are also available
Megastore Telephone Nº: 0371 811 1955

GROUND INFORMATION

Away Supporters' Entrances & Sections:
Shed End

ADMISSION INFO (2019/2020 PRICES)

Adult Seating: £30.00 – £95.00
Child/Senior Citizen Seating: £18.00 – £27.50
Note: Concessionary tickets are available in the Family Stand, East Upper Stand, Shed Lower and Matthew Harding Lower stands.
Programme Price: £3.00

FANS WITH DISABILITIES INFORMATION

Seating: 258 spaces in total (including personal assistants) for Home and Away fans in the disabled area
Personal Assistants: One admitted per fan with disabilities
Prices: Free of charge for fans with disabilities
Disabled Toilets: Available in the East Stand Concourse, West Stand and also in the Matthew Harding Stand (Radar Key required for access).
Free commentaries for blind supporters are available
Contact: 0371 811-2012 (Bookings are necessary)

Travelling Supporters' Information:
Routes: From the North & East: Follow Central London signs from the A1/M1 to Hyde Park Corner, then signs for Guildford (A3) to Knightsbridge (A4). After 1 mile turn left into Fulham Road; From the South: Take the A13 or A24 then the A219 to cross Putney Bridge and follow signs for 'West End' (A304) to join the A308 into Fulham Road; From the West: Take the M4 then A4 to Central London, then follow signs to Westminster (A3220). After ¾ mile, turn right at crossroads into Fulham Road.

CHELTENHAM TOWN FC

Founded: 1887
Nickname: 'Robins'
Ground: Jonny-Rocks Stadium, Whaddon Road, Cheltenham, Gloucestershire GL52 5NA
Ground Capacity: 7,200
Seating Capacity: 4,054
Record Attendance: 8,326 (1956)

Pitch Size: 110 × 72 yards
Colours: Red and White striped shirts, White shorts
Telephone Nº: (01242) 573558
Fax Number: (01242) 224675
Web Site: www.ctfc.com
E-mail: info@ctfc.com

GENERAL INFORMATION

Car Parking: Available at the ground for a £5.00 charge
Coach Parking: Please phone for details
Nearest Railway Station: Cheltenham Spa (2½ miles)
Nearest Bus Station: Cheltenham Royal Well
Club Shop: At the ground
Opening Times: Tuesday, Thursday and Friday 10.00am to 3.00pm. Also Saturday Matchdays from 12.00pm.
Telephone Nº: (01242) 573558 Option 2

GROUND INFORMATION

Away Supporters' Entrances & Sections:
Hazlewoods Stand (entrance from Whaddon Road)

ADMISSION INFO (2019/2020 PRICES)

Adult Standing: £17.00
Adult Seating: £21.00 or £22.00
Junior/Student Standing: £6.00
Junior/Student Seating: £8.00
Concessionary Standing: £13.00
Concessionary Seating: £15.00 or £16.00
Programme Price: £3.00

FANS WITH DISABILITIES INFORMATION

Wheelchairs: Accommodated in front of the Main Stand (use main entrance) and in the Colin Farmer Stand
Helpers: Admitted free of charge
Prices: Concessionary prices are charged
Disabled Toilets: Available in the Colin Farmer Stand, adjacent to the Main Stand and in the Social Club
Contact: (01242) 573558 (Bookings are necessary)

Travelling Supporters' Information:
Routes: The ground is situated to the North-East of Cheltenham, 1 mile from the Town Centre off the B4632 (Prestbury Road) – Whaddon Road is to the East of the B4632 just North of Pittville Circus. Road signs in the vicinity indicate 'Whaddon Road/ Cheltenham Town FC'.

COLCHESTER UNITED FC

Founded: 1937 (**Entered League**: 1950)
Former Names: The Eagles FC & Colchester Town FC
Nickname: 'U's'
Ground: Jobserve Community Stadium, United Way, Colchester CO4 5UP
Ground Capacity: 10,105 (All seats)
Record Attendance: 19,042 (27/11/48 – Layer Road)
Pitch Size: 112 × 72 yards

Colours: Royal blue and white striped shirts with White shorts
Telephone N°: (01206) 755100
Ticket Office: (01206) 755161
Fax Number: (01206) 715327
Web Site: www.cu-fc.com
E-mail: ticketing@colchesterunited.net

GENERAL INFORMATION

Car Parking: 700 spaces at the ground – pre-bookings only. The club recommends fans should use the Matchday shuttle bus service (cost £1.50) where possible. This runs from Bruff Close, near Colchester North Railway Station where there is a large car park for all fans.
Coach Parking: Drivers should liaise with with stewards upon arrival at the ground
Nearest Railway Station: Colchester North (1½ miles)
Nearest Bus Station: Colchester Town Centre (1½ miles)
Club Shop: At the ground
Opening Times: Weekdays 10.00am to 2.00pm, Saturday Matchdays 11.00am to 6.00pm and Midweek Matchdays 5.30pm to 10.00pm.
Telephone N°: (01206) 755135

GROUND INFORMATION

Away Supporters' Entrances & Sections:
North Stand or East Stand (North End)

ADMISSION INFO (2019/2020 PRICES)

Adult Seating: £22.00 – £30.00
Concessionary Seating: £17.00 – £24.00
Ages 18 to 21 Seating: £18.00
Under-18s Seating: £13.50 – £16.50
Under-14s Seating: £5.50 – £8.50
Under-11s Seating: Free of charge
Note: A variety of discounted rates are available for tickets purchased a set number of weeks in advance of the game.
Programme Price: £3.00 (Free to ticket holders)

FANS WITH DISABILITIES INFORMATION

Wheelchairs: 40 spaces in total situated in all stands with lift access available where required.
Helpers: One helper admitted per wheelchair
Prices: Concessionary prices for fans with disabilities. Helpers are admitted free of charge.
Disabled Toilets: Available in each stand
Contact: (01206) 755161 or (01206) 755130 (Disability Liaison Officer: chris.saward@colchesterunited.net)

Travelling Supporters' Information:
Routes: The stadium is located at junction 28 of the A12 on the northern outskirts of Colchester. As parking near the stadium is very limited, the club recommends both home and away fans should use the Matchday shuttle bus service which runs from Bruff Close, near to Colchester North Station where there is a large car park. Alternatively, pre-book a space in the club car park.

COVENTRY CITY FC

Coventry City are playing at Birmingham City's St. Andrew's Stadium during the 2019/2020 season.

Founded: 1883 (**Entered League**: 1919)
Former Names: Singers FC (1883-1898)
Nickname: 'Sky Blues'
Ground: St. Andrew's Trillion Trophy Stadium, Birmingham B9 4RL
Ground Capacity: 29,409 (All seats)
Record Attendance: 51,455 (vs Wolverhampton Wanderers at Highfield Road on29th April 1967)

Pitch Size: 109 × 74 yards
Colours: Sky Blue shirts and socks, White shorts
Telephone Nº: (024) 7699-1987
Ticket Office: (024) 7699-1987
Postal Address: Sky Blue Lodge, Leamington Road, Ryton-on-Dunsmore, Coventry CV8 3FL
Web Site: www.ccfc.co.uk
E-mail: info@ccfc.co.uk

GENERAL INFORMATION

Car Parking: Street Parking + Birmingham Wheels (secure parking but not related to the club)
Coach Parking: Coventry Road
Nearest Railway Station: Birmingham New Street or Birmingham Moor Street (20 minutes walk)
Nearest Bus Station: Digbeth National Express Coach Station
Club Shops: At Arena Shopping Park, Classic Drive, Coventry CV6 6AS
Opening Times: Monday to Saturday 9.30am to 5.30pm (unntil 8.00pm on Thursdays) and Sunday 10.30am to 4.30pm
Telephone Nº: (024) 7767-2021

GROUND INFORMATION

Away Supporters' Entrances & Sections:
Gil Merrick Stand, Coventry Road

ADMISSION INFO (2019/2020 PRICES)

Adult Seating: £20.00
Under-18s Seating: £10.00
Concessionary Seating: £15.00
Programme Price: £3.00

DISABLED INFORMATION

Wheelchairs: Spaces available in the Spion Kop Stand, Gil Merrick Lower Stand, Tilton Road Stand and West Paddocks
Helpers: One assistant admitted for each fan with disabilities
Prices: Normal prices apply for fans with disabilities. Helpers are admitted free of charge
Disabled Toilets: Available in the Spion Kop Stand, Family Stand, Gil Merrick Stand and Tilton Road Stand
Contact: (024) 7699-2335 – mark.hornby@ccfc.co.uk

Travelling Supporters' Information: From All Parts: Exit M6 at Junction 6 and take the A38 (M) (Aston Expressway). Leave at 2nd exit then take first exit at roundabout along the Dartmouth Middleway. After 1¼ miles turn left on to Coventry Road.
Bus Services: Services 17, 58, 59 & 60 from Birmingham Centre stop at Cattell Road just to the south of the stadium and Services 97f stops at Garrison Lane just to the north of the stadium.

CRAWLEY TOWN FC

Founded: 1896 (**Entered League**: 2011)
Former Names: None
Nickname: 'Red Devils'
Ground: The People's Pension Stadium, Winfield Way, Crawley, West Sussex RH11 9RX
Record Attendance: 5,880 (2013)
Pitch Size: 113 × 72 yards

Colours: Red shirts and shorts
Telephone Nº: (01293) 410000 (Ground)
Ticket Office: (01293) 410005
Fax Number: (01293) 410002
Ground Capacity: 5,996 **Seating Capacity**: 3,295
Web site: www.crawleytownfc.com
E-mail: feedback@crawleytownfc.com

GENERAL INFORMATION

Car Parking: A number of pre-booked spaces are available at the ground for £5.00 (contact the club). Otherwise, free parking is available at Broadfield Park (5 minutes walk).
Coach Parking: At the ground
Nearest Railway Station: Crawley (1 mile)
Nearest Bus Station: By the Railway Station
Club Shop: At the ground
Opening Times: Weekdays 9.00am to 4.30pm (closed on Wednesdays) and Saturday matchdays from 10.00am onwards. Mid-week matches also open from 6.00pm to kick-off then for 30 minutes after the game.
Telephone Nº: (01293) 410000

GROUND INFORMATION

Away Supporters' Entrances & Sections:
North Entrance for both terrace and seating

ADMISSION INFO (2019/2020 PRICES)

Adult Standing: £16.00
Adult Seating: £20.00 – £22.00
Under-21s Standing: £11.00
Under-21s Seating: £13.00 – £14.00
Under-18s Standing/Seating: £10.00
Under-16s Standing/Seating: £4.00
Under-11s Standing/Seating: £1.00
Senior Citizen Standing: £12.00
Senior Citizen Seating: £15.00 – £18.00
Programme Price: £3.00

FANS WITH DISABILITIES INFORMATION

Wheelchairs: Accommodated in a special section of the Main Stand (Lift access available)
Helpers: One helper admitted per fan with disabilities
Prices: Normal prices apply for fans with disabilities. Free of charge for helpers
Disabled Toilets: Available
Contact: (01293) 410000 (Bookings are necessary)

Travelling Supporters' Information:
Routes: Exit the M23 at Junction 11 and take the A23 towards Crawley. After ¼ mile, the Stadium is on the left. Take the first exit at the roundabout for the Stadium entrance.

CREWE ALEXANDRA FC

Founded: 1877 (**Entered League**: 1892)
Nickname: 'Railwaymen'
Ground: Alexandra Stadium, Gresty Road, Crewe, Cheshire CW2 6EB
Ground Capacity: 10,101 (All seats)
Record Attendance: 20,000 (30th January 1960)
Pitch Size: 100 × 73 yards

Colours: Red shirts with White shorts
Telephone Nº: (01270) 213014
Ticket Office: (01270) 252610
Fax Number: (01270) 216320
Web Site: www.crewealex.net
E-mail: info@crewealex.net

GENERAL INFORMATION

Car Parking: Car Park at the ground (spaces for 400 cars with a £3.50 fee)
Coach Parking: Car Park at the ground
Nearest Railway Station: Crewe (5 minutes walk)
Nearest Bus Station: Crewe Town
Club Shop: At the ground
Opening Times: Monday to Friday and Matchdays 9.00am – 5.00pm (until 7.45pm for Night matches)
Telephone Nº: (01270) 213014 extension 101

GROUND INFORMATION

Away Supporters' Entrances & Sections:
Whitby Morrison Ice Cream Van Stand

ADMISSION INFO (2019/2020 PRICES)

Adult Seating: £20.00 – £22.00
Senior Citizen Seating: £15.50 – £17.00
Under-17s Seating: £9.50 – £10.50
Under-11s Seating: £6.00 – £6.50
Note: Members qualify for cheaper prices. Family tickets are available in the Family Stand.
Programme Price: £3.00

FANS WITH DISABILITIES INFORMATION

Wheelchairs: Over 70 spaces are available for home fans and 14 spaces are available for away fans
Helpers: One helper admitted per fan with disabilities
Prices: £17.00 for each fan with disabilities and one helper
Disabled Toilets: Available in all Stands
Commentaries are available for the blind
Contact: (01270) 252610 or (01270) 213014 Ext. 3100
Beverley Dyer – bdyer@crewealex.net (Bookings necessary)

Travelling Supporters' Information:
Routes: From the North: Exit the M6 at Junction 17 and take the Crewe (A534) road, and at Crewe roundabout follow signs for Chester into Nantwich Road. Then take a left turn into Gresty Road; From the South and East: Take the A52 to the A5020, then on to Crewe roundabout (then as from the North); From the West: Take the A534 into Crewe and turn right just before the railway station into Gresty Road. **SatNav users**: Please enter the following post code: CW2 6EB

CRYSTAL PALACE FC

Photo courtesy of Crystal Palace FC

Founded: 1905 (**Entered League**: 1920)
Nickname: 'Eagles'
Ground: Selhurst Park, Whitehorse Lane, London, SE25 6PU
Ground Capacity: 25,486 (All seats)
Record Attendance: 51,482 (11th May 1979)
Pitch Size: 110 × 74 yards

Colours: Red and Blue striped shirts with Blue shorts
Telephone Nº: (020) 8768-6000
Ticket Office: 0871 200-0071
Fax Number: (020) 8771-5311
Web Site: www.cpfc.co.uk
E-mail: reception@cpfc.co.uk

GENERAL INFORMATION

Car Parking: Street Parking only
Coach Parking: Thornton Heath
Nearest Railway Station: Selhurst or Norwood Junction (both 5 minutes walk)
Nearest Bus Station: West Croydon
Club Shop: At the ground
Opening Times: Weekdays & Away Matchdays 9.00am to 5.30pm. Home Matchdays from 9.00am until 30 minutes after kick-off as well as 60 minutes after the final whistle.
Telephone Nº: (020) 8768-6100

GROUND INFORMATION

Away Supporters' Entrances & Sections:
Park Road for the Arthur Wait Stand

ADMISSION INFO (2019/2020 PRICES)

Adult Seating: £30.00 – £53.00
Concessionary Seating: £25.00 – £38.00
Junior Seating: £10.00 – £26.00
Note: Prices vary depending on the category of the game
Programme Price: £3.00

FANS WITH DISABILITIES INFORMATION

Wheelchairs: Spaces are available in a special area in the Holmesdale Road Stand and also in the Arthur Wait Stand
Helpers: One helper admitted per wheelchair
Prices: Concessionary prices apply for fans with disabilities. Helpers are admitted free of charge
Disabled Toilets: Located in the Holmesdale Road Stand
Commentaries are available for 12 people
Contact: (020) 8768-6080 pam.groves@cpfc.co.uk
(Bookings are necessary)

Travelling Supporters' Information:
Routes: From the North: Take the M1/A1 to the North Circular (A406) for Chiswick. Take the South Circular (A205) to Wandsworth then the A3 to the A214 and follow signs for Streatham to the A23. Turn left onto the B273 after 1 mile, follow to the end, turn left into the High Street and then into Whitehorse Lane; From the East: Take the A232 (Croydon Road) to Shirley and join the A215 (Northwood Road). After 2¼ miles turn left into Whitehorse Lane; From the South: Take the A23 and follow signs for Crystal Palace (B266) through Thornton Heath into Whitehorse Lane; From the West: Take the M4 to Chiswick (then as North).

DERBY COUNTY FC

Founded: 1884 (**Entered League**: 1888)
Nickname: 'Rams'
Ground: Pride Park Stadium, Royal Way, Pride Park, Derby DE24 8XL
Ground Capacity: 33,597 (All seats)
Record Attendance: 33,597 (25th May 2001)
Pitch Size: 110 × 74 yards

Colours: White shirts with Black shorts
Telephone Nº: 0871 472-1884
Ticket Office: 0871 472-1884 Option 1
Fax Number: (01332) 667519
Web Site: www.dcfc.co.uk
E-mail: derby.county@dcfc.co.uk

GENERAL INFORMATION

Car Parking: Spaces for 1,424 cars at the ground (available for permit holders only)
Coach Parking: At the ground
Nearest Railway Station: Derby (1 mile)
Nearest Bus Station: Derby Central
Club Shop: DCFC Megastore at the ground
Opening Times: Monday to Saturday 9.00am – 5.00pm (from 10.00am on Tuesdays); Sundays 10.00am – 4.00pm
Telephone Nº: 0871 472-1884 (Option 2)

GROUND INFORMATION

Away Supporters' Entrances & Sections:
South East Corner

ADMISSION INFO (2019/2020 PRICES)

Due to the introduction of a 'dynamic' pricing system, we suggest that fans contact the club for further details about admission prices for any particular game.
Programme Price: £3.00

FANS WITH DISABILITIES INFORMATION

Wheelchairs: 206 spaces available in total
Helpers: One helper admitted for each fan with disabilities
Prices: Please contact the club for further information
Disabled Toilets: Yes
Contact: (01332) 821044 Emma Drury (Bookings are necessary)

Travelling Supporters' Information:
Routes: From All Parts: Exit the M1 at Junction 25 and follow the A52 towards the City Centre until the ground is signposted on the left. Follow the signs for the ground.
From the Train Station: The Stadium is 10 minutes walk by way of a tunnel under the railway opposite Brunswick Inn, Station Approach. Then follow the footpath; Buses: A shuttle service runs from the bus station from 1.00pm until 2.45pm on Saturdays. A similar service runs from 6.00pm – 7.30pm for midweek games. Return shuttles are available post-match.

DONCASTER ROVERS FC

Founded: 1879
Former Names: None
Nickname: 'Rovers'
Ground: Keepmoat Stadium, Stadium Way, Doncaster DN4 5JW
Record Attendance: 15,001 (1st April 2008)
Pitch Size: 110 × 72 yards

Colours: Red & White hooped shirts with White shorts
Telephone Nº: (01302) 764664
Ticket Office: (01302) 762576
Fax Number: (01302) 363525
Ground Capacity: 15,231 (All seats)
Web site: www.doncasterroversfc.co.uk
E-mail: info@clubdoncaster.co.uk

GENERAL INFORMATION

Car Parking: 1,000 spaces available at the ground (£5.00)
Coach Parking: At the ground (£20.00 fee)
Nearest Railway Station: Doncaster (2 miles)
Nearest Bus Station: Doncaster (2 miles)
Club Shop: At the ground
Opening Times: Monday to Saturday 10.00am to 4.00pm (until 8.00pm for midweek matches). Saturday Matchdays open 10.00am to kick-off then from full-time until 5.30pm.
Telephone Nº: (01302) 764667

GROUND INFORMATION

Away Supporters' Entrances & Sections:
North Stand

ADMISSION INFO (2019/2020 PRICES)

Adult Seating: £21.00 – £22.00
Senior Citizen/Ages 22 to 24 Seating: £17.00 – £18.00
Ages 18 to 21 Seating: £13.00 – £14.00
Ages 12 to 17 Seating: £8.00
Under-12s Seating: £5.00
Note: Members prices are lower than those shown.
Programme Price: £3.00

FANS WITH DISABILITIES INFORMATION

Wheelchairs: 18 spaces available in total with Away fans accommodated in the North Stand
Helpers: Admitted
Prices: Normal prices for fans with disabilities. Helpers are admitted free of charge
Disabled Toilets: Available in all Stands (Radar Key required)
Contact: (01302) 764664 (Bookings are necessary)

Travelling Supporters' Information:
Routes: Exit the M18 at Junction 3 and follow the A6182 towards Doncaster. The stadium is approximately 1½ miles from the motorway and is well signposted so follow these signs. There are 1,000 car parking spaces available at the stadium and the cost is £5.00 per car. A number of businesses on the nearby business park also offer matchday parking for a similar charge.
Bus services run from the town centre/interchange to the Stadium with a shuttle service back operating after the match.

EVERTON FC

Founded: 1878 (**Entered League**: 1888)
Former Names: St. Domingo's FC (1878-79)
Nickname: 'The Toffees'
Ground: Goodison Park, Goodison Road, Liverpool L4 4EL
Ground Capacity: 39,572 (All seats)
Record Attendance: 78,299 (18th September 1948)

Pitch Size: 110 × 74 yards
Colours: Blue shirts with White shorts
Telephone Nº: (0151) 556-1878
Ticket Office: (0151) 556-1878
Fax Number: (0151) 286-9112
Web Site: www.evertonfc.com
E-mail: everton@evertonfc.com

GENERAL INFORMATION

Car Parking: Corner of Priory Road and Utting Avenue
Coach Parking: Priory Road
Nearest Railway Station: Kirkdale
Nearest Mainline Railway Station: Liverpool Lime Street
Nearest Bus Station: Queen's Square, Liverpool
Club Shop: 'Megastore' in Walton Lane by the ground and also at the Liverpool One Shopping Complex.
Opening Times: Megastore: Monday to Saturday 9.00am to 6.00pm and Sundays 10.00am to 4.00pm. Liverpool One: Weekdays 9.30am to 7.00pm, Saturdays 9.00am to 7.00pm and Sundays 11.00am to 5.00pm.
Telephone Nº: (0151) 556-1878

GROUND INFORMATION

Away Supporters' Entrances & Sections:
Bullens Road entrances for Bullens Stand – Turnstiles 55-60

ADMISSION INFO (2019/2020 PRICES)

Adult Seating: £35.00 – £49.00
Junior Seating: £15.00 – £20.00
Senior Citizen Seating: £30.00

FANS WITH DISABILITIES INFORMATION

Wheelchairs: 153 spaces for home fans, 19 spaces for away fans in a special section.
Helpers: One helper admitted per wheelchair
Prices: Normal prices for fans with disabilities. Helpers free.
Disabled Toilets: Available in the section for disabled fans – Radar Key required (available from stewards if necessary).
Commentaries are available for the blind
Contact: (0151) 556-1878 or (0151) 530-5396
(Bookings are necessary)

Travelling Supporters' Information:
Routes: From the North: Exit the M6 at Junction 26 onto the M58 and continue to it's end. Take the 2nd exit at the roundabout onto the A59 Ormskirk Road. Continue along into Rice Lane and go straight across at the next roundabout into County Road. After ½ mile, turn left into Everton Valley then bear left into Walton Lane for the ground; From the South & East: Exit the M6 at Junction 21A and take the M62 to it's end. Turn right at traffic lights onto A5088 Queen Drive and continue to the junction with Walton Hall Avenue then turn left into Walton Lane (A580) and the ground is on the right.
Bus Services: Services to the ground – 19, 20, F1, F2, 30

EXETER CITY FC

Founded: 1901 (**Re-Entered League**: 2008)
Former Names: Formed by the amalgamation of St. Sidwell United FC & Exeter United FC
Nickname: 'The Grecians'
Ground: St. James Park, Exeter, EX4 6PX
Ground Capacity: 8,696
Seating Capacity: 3,600
Record Attendance: 21,013 (4th March 1931)

Pitch Size: 114 × 73 yards
Colours: Red and White striped shirts, Black shorts
Telephone Nº: (01392) 411243
Ticket Office: (01392) 411243
Fax Number: (01392) 413959
Web Site: www.exetercityfc.co.uk
E-mail: reception@ecfc.co.uk

GENERAL INFORMATION

Car Parking: Parr Street, John Lewis and Bampfyled Street car parks
Coach Parking: Paris Street Bus Station (10 minute walk)
Nearest Railway Station: Exeter St. James Park (adjacent)
Nearest Bus Station: Paris Street Bus Station
Club Shop: At the ground
Opening Times: Monday to Friday 8.30am to 5.00pm and 11.00am to 5.30pm on matchdays.
Club Shop Telephone Nº: (01392) 413958

GROUND INFORMATION

Away Supporters' Entrances & Sections:
St. James Road turnstiles for standing in the Marsh Kia St. James Road Stand or Blocks L and M of the IP Office Main Stand for seating.
Note: Cash is only taken on the Thatcher Gold Big Bank turnstiles. Away section tickets are sold at the booth adjacent to the St. James Road turnstiles.

ADMISSION INFO (2019/2020 PRICES)

Adult Standing: £17.00 – £18.00
Adult Seating: £23.00 – £24.00
Concessionary Standing: £14.00 – £15.00
Concessionary Seating: £20.00 – £21.00
Under-18s Standing: £6.00 – £7.00
Under-18s Seating: £11.00 – £12.00
Programme Price: £3.00

FANS WITH DISABILITIES INFORMATION

Wheelchairs: Accommodated in the IP Office Main Stand and the Big Bank.
Helpers: One assistant admitted per wheelchair
Prices: Free of charge for assistants. £14.00 – £20.00 for fans with disabilities in the wheelchair area.
Disabled Toilets: Available by the Big Bank Stand
Contact: (01392) 411243 (Bookings are necessary)

Travelling Supporters' Information:
Routes: From the North: Exit the M5 at Junction 29 and follow signs to the City Centre along Heavitree Road. Take the 4th exit at the roundabout into Western Way and the 2nd exit into Tiverton Road then 2nd left into Stadium Way; From the East: Take the A30 into Heavitree Road (then as from the North); From the South & West: Take the A38 and follow City Centre signs into Western Way, then take the third exit at the roundabout into St. James Road. (Follow the brown football signs from the M5)
Note: This ground is difficult to find being in a residential area on the side of a hill without prominent floodlights!

FLEETWOOD TOWN FC

Founded: 1997 (**Entered League**: 2012)
Former Names: Fleetwood FC (1908-1976), Fleetwood Town FC (1977-1996), Fleetwood Freeport FC (1997-2002)
Nickname: 'Cod Army'
Ground: Highbury Stadium, Park Avenue, Fleetwood FY7 6TX
Record Attendance: 6,150 vs Rochdale (13/11/65)
Pitch Size: 110 × 71 yards

Colours: Red shirts with White Arms, White shorts
Telephone N°: (01253) 775080
Fax Number: (01253) 775081
Ground Capacity: 5,327
Seating Capacity: 2,701
Web site: www.fleetwoodtownfc.com
E-mail: info@fleetwoodtownfc.com

GENERAL INFORMATION

Car Parking: Street parking only
Coach Parking: Contact the club for information
Nearest Railway Station: Poulton-le-Fylde (7 miles)
Nearest Bus Station: None
Nearest Tram Stop from Blackpool: Stanley Road
Club Shop: At the ground
Opening Times: Monday to Friday 9.00am to 5.00pm
Telephone N°: (01253) 775080

GROUND INFORMATION

Away Supporters' Entrances & Sections:
Standing in the Percy Ronson stand and seating in the Parkside Stand

ADMISSION INFO (2019/2020 PRICES)

Adult Standing: £20.00 – £24.00
Adult Seating: £22.00 – £28.00
Senior Citizen/Under-25s Standing: £15.00 – £19.00
Senior Citizen/Under-25s Seating: £17.00 – £23.00
Under-16s Standing: £5.00 – £9.00
Under-16s Seating: £6.00 – £11.00
Note: Prices are cheaper for members

FANS WITH DISABILITIES INFORMATION

Wheelchairs: Accommodated
Helpers: Admitted
Prices: Normal prices for the fans with disabilities. Free of charge for helpers
Disabled Toilets: Available
Contact: (01253) 775080 (Bookings are necessary)

Travelling Supporters' Information:
Routes: Exit the M6 at Junction 32 and take the M55 towards Blackpool. Exit the M55 at Junction 3 and follow the A585 towards Fleetwood for approximately 11½ miles. On the outskirts of town, you will reach a roundabout with Blackpool and Fylde college on your left. Continue straight on at this roundabout but then take the first turn on the left into Copse Road. After approximately 1 mile, branch left and turn left onto Radcliffe Road as you pass the Fire Station. Take the next right onto Stanley Road and the Stadium is at the bottom of the road on the left.

FOREST GREEN ROVERS FC

Founded: 1889 (**Entered League**: 2017)
Former Names: Stroud FC
Nickname: 'The Green Devils'
Ground: The New Lawn, Another Way, Forest Green, Nailsworth, Gloucestershire, GL6 0FG
Record Attendance: 4,836 (3rd January 2009)
Pitch Size: 110 × 70 yards

Colours: Green and Black hooped shirts, Green shorts
Telephone Nº: 0333 123-1889
Ticket Office: 0333 123-1889
Fax Number: (01453) 835291
Ground Capacity: 5,141
Seating Capacity: 2,000
Web site: www.fgr.co.uk
E-mail: reception@fgr.co.uk

GENERAL INFORMATION

Car Parking: At the ground
Coach Parking: At the ground
Nearest Railway Station: Stroud (4 miles)
Nearest Bus Station: Nailsworth
Club Shop: At the ground
Opening Times: Monday to Friday 9.00am to 3.00pm
Telephone Nº: 0333 123-1889

GROUND INFORMATION

Away Supporters' Entrances & Sections:
EESI Stand (West Stand)

ADMISSION INFO (2019/2020 PRICES)

Adult Standing: £18.00 **Adult Seating**: £23.00–£25.00
Senior Citizen Standing: £14.00
Senior Citizen Seating: £18.00 – £20.00
Under-16s Standing: £6.00
Under-16s Seating: £8.00 – £9.00
Under-11s Standing/Seating: Free of charge – £4.00
Under-21s Standing: £9.00
Under-21s Seating: £12.00 – £14.00
Note: Discounted prices are available for advance purchases

FANS WITH DISABILITIES INFORMATION

Wheelchairs: Accommodated in the Main Stand
Helpers: Admitted
Prices: Normal prices for fans with disabilities. Helpers free
Disabled Toilets: Available
Contact: 0333 123-1889 (Enquiries are required at least 72 hours in advance of the game)

Travelling Supporters' Information:
Routes: The ground is located 4 miles south of Stroud on the A46 to Bath. Upon entering Nailsworth, turn into Spring Hill at the mini-roundabout and the ground is approximately ½ mile up the hill on the left.

FULHAM FC

Founded: 1879 (**Entered League**: 1907)
Former Names: Fulham St.Andrew's FC (1879-1898)
Nickname: 'The Whites'
Ground: Craven Cottage, Stevenage Road, Fulham, London SW6 6HH
Ground Capacity: 19,000 (All seats – temporarily reduced due to redevelopment of the Riverside Stand)
Record Attendance: 49,335 (8th October 1938)

Pitch Size: 109 × 71 yards
Colours: White shirts with Black shorts
Telephone Nº: 0843 208-1222
Ticket Office: (020) 3871-0810
Fax Number: 0870 442-0236
Web Site: www.fulhamfc.com
E-mail: enquiries@fulhamfc.com

GENERAL INFORMATION

Car Parking: Street Parking (Matchday restrictions apply)
Coach Parking: Stevenage Road/Fulham Palace Road
Nearest Railway Station: Putney (1 mile)
Nearest Tube Station: Putney Bridge (District) (1 mile)
Club Shop: At the ground and also 959-961 Fulham Road, SW6 5HY
Opening Times: At the ground: Monday to Saturday 9.00am to 5.00pm and Sundays 11.00am to 4.00pm
Telephone Nº: 0843 208-1223

GROUND INFORMATION

Away Supporters' Entrances & Sections:
Putney End for the Putney Stand

ADMISSION INFO (2019/2020 PRICES)

Adult Seating: £30.00 – £45.00
Junior Seating: £15.00
Concessionary/Under-21s Seating: £25.00 – £40.00
Note: Prices vary depending on the category of the game and tickets may be cheaper if purchased in advance.
Programme Price: £3.50

FANS WITH DISABILITIES INFORMATION

Wheelchairs: 63 spaces in total with and 20 spaces for Away fans in the Putney End, Block 7, Gate 1
Helpers: One assistant admitted per fan with disabilities
Prices: Concessionary prices for fans with disabilities. One helper admitted free of charge for each fan in a wheelchair.
Disabled Toilets: Available – access via Radar Key system.
Contact: (020) 3871-0810 (Bookings necessary)
Disability Liaison Officer: Nicola Walworth contact on (020) 8336-7477 or via E-mail – nwalworth@fulhamfc.com

Travelling Supporters' Information:
Routes: From the North: Take the A1/M1 to the North Circular (A406), travel west to Neasden and follow signs for Harlesden A404, then Hammersmith A219. At Broadway, follow the Fulham sign and turn right after 1 mile into Harbord Street then left at the end for the ground; From the South & East: Take the South Circular (A205), follow the Putney Bridge sign (A219). Cross the bridge and follow Hammersmith signs for ½ mile, turn left into Bishops Park Road, then right at the end; From the West: Take the M4 to the A4. Branch left after 2 miles into Hammersmith Broadway (then as from the North).

GILLINGHAM FC

Founded: 1893 (**Entered League**: 1920)
Former Names: New Brompton FC (1893-1913)
Nickname: 'Gills'
Ground: MEMS Priestfield Stadium, Redfern Avenue, Gillingham, Kent ME7 4DD
Ground Capacity: 11,582 (All seats)
Record Attendance: 23,002 (10th January 1948)

Pitch Size: 110 × 70 yards
Telephone Nº: (01634) 300000
Ticket Office: (01634) 300000
Fax Number: (01634) 850986
Web Site: www.gillinghamfootballclub.com
E-mail: enquiries@priestfield.com

GENERAL INFORMATION

Car Parking: Street parking
Coach Parking: Croneen's Yard Car Park in Railway Street (5 minute walk)
Nearest Railway Station: Gillingham
Nearest Bus Station: Gillingham
Club Shop: Megastore in Redfern Avenue
Opening Times: Megastore is open Weekdays from 9.00am to 5.00pm and Matchdays from 9.00am to 3.00pm
Telephone Nº: (01634) 300000

GROUND INFORMATION

Away Supporters' Entrances & Sections:
Priestfield Road End

ADMISSION INFO (2019/2020 PRICES)

Adult Seating: £24.00 – £27.00
Senior Citizen Seating: £21.00 – £27.00
Under-18s Seating: £8.00 – £9.00
Under-12s Seating: £8.00 – £9.00
Note: Tickets are £2.00 cheaper if purchased in advance
Programme Price: £3.00

FANS WITH DISABILITIES INFORMATION

Wheelchairs: 67 spaces in total for Home and Away fans and helpers in special sections around the ground
Helpers: One helper admitted per fan with disabilities
Prices: Normal prices for fans with disabilities. Helpers free
Disabled Toilets: Available in all areas of the ground
Contact: (01634) 300000 (Bookings are necessary)
Disability Liaison Officer: b.reeves@priestfield.com

Travelling Supporters' Information:
Routes: From All Parts: Exit the M2 at Junction 4 and follow the link road (dual carriageway) B278 to the 3rd roundabout. Turn left onto the A2 (dual carriageway) and go across the roundabout to the traffic lights. Turn right into Woodlands Road after the traffic lights. The ground is ¼ mile on the left.

GRIMSBY TOWN FC

Founded: 1878
Former Names: Grimsby Pelham FC (1879)
Nickname: 'Mariners'
Ground: Blundell Park, Cleethorpes DN35 7PY
Ground Capacity: 8,933 (All seats)
Record Attendance: 31,651 (20th February 1937)
Pitch Size: 111 × 74 yards

Colours: Black and White striped shirts, Black shorts
Telephone Nº: (01472) 605050
Ticket Office: (01472) 605050 (Option 4)
Fax Number: (01472) 693665
Web Site: www.grimsby-townfc.co.uk
E-mail: enquiries@gtfc.co.uk

GENERAL INFORMATION

Car Parking: Street parking
Coach Parking: Harrington Street – near the ground
Nearest Railway Station: Cleethorpes (1½ miles)
Nearest Bus Station: Brighowgate, Grimsby (4 miles)
Club Shop: At the ground
Opening Times: Monday – Friday 9.00am to 5.00pm; Matchday Saturdays 9.00am to kick-off
Telephone Nº: (01472) 605050

GROUND INFORMATION

Away Supporters' Entrances & Sections:
Harrington Street turnstiles 15-18 and Constitution Avenue turnstiles 5-14 for accommodation in the Osmond Stand

ADMISSION INFO (2019/2020 PRICES)

Adult Seating: £22.00
Senior Citizen/Student Seating: £15.00
Young Adults Seating (Ages 15–18): £15.00
Child Seating: £5.00 – £7.00 (Under-15s)
Note: Tickets are cheaper if purchased before the matchday

FANS WITH DISABILITIES INFORMATION

Wheelchairs: 20 spaces for home fans in the Main Stand and 20 spaces for away fans in the Osmond Stand
Helpers: Helpers are admitted
Prices: Normal prices for fans with disabilities. Helpers free
Disabled Toilets: Available
Commentaries are also available
Contact: (01472) 605050 (Bookings are necessary) or E-mail the Supporters' Liaison Officer – slo@gtfc.co.uk

Travelling Supporters' Information:
Routes: From All Parts except Lincolnshire and East Anglia: Take the M180 to the A180 and follow signs for Grimsby/Cleethorpes. The A180 ends at a roundabout (the 3rd in short distance after crossing docks), take the 2nd exit from the roundabout over the Railway flyover into Cleethorpes Road (A1098) and continue into Grimsby Road. After the second stretch of dual carriageway, the ground is ½ mile on the left; From Lincolnshire: Take the A46 or A16 and follow Cleethorpes signs along (A1098) Weelsby Road for 2 miles. Take the 1st exit at the roundabout at the end of Clee Road into Grimsby Road. The ground is 1¾ miles on the right.

HUDDERSFIELD TOWN FC

Founded: 1908 (**Entered League**: 1910)
Nickname: 'Terriers'
Ground: The John Smith's Stadium, Huddersfield, HD1 6PX
Ground Capacity: 24,554 (All seats)
Record Attendance: 24,169 (30th September 2017)
Pitch Size: 115 × 76 yards

Colours: Blue and White striped shirts, White shorts and socks
Telephone Nº: (01484) 960600
Ticket Office: (01484) 960606
Fax Number: (01484) 484101
Web Site: www.htafc.com
E-mail: info@htafc.com

GENERAL INFORMATION

Car Parking: No spaces available at the ground but private car parks on Leeds Road and St. Andrew's Road (not associated with the club) charge around £6.00 to park.
Coach Parking: Adjacent car park
Nearest Railway Station: Huddersfield (1¼ miles)
Nearest Bus Station: Huddersfield
Club Shop: At the ground and in the Packhorse Shopping Centre in King Street, Huddersfield
Opening Times: At the ground: Monday to Saturday 9.00am to 5.00pm, Saturday Matchdays 9.00am to 3.00pm. Packhorse Centre: Monday to Saturday 9.00am to 5.00pm
Telephone Nº: (01484) 960636 or (01484) 430192

GROUND INFORMATION

Away Supporters' Entrances & Sections:
Adzorb South Stand

ADMISSION INFO (2019/2020 PRICES)

Adult Seating: £30.00
Under-18s Seating: £15.00
Under-8s Seating: £10.00
Concessionary Seating: £20.00
Note: Prices shown are for tickets purchased in advance.
Programme Price: £3.50

FANS WITH DISABILITIES INFORMATION

Wheelchairs: 177 spaces in total for home and away fans in the special sections in the Adzorb South Stand, Revell Ward Stand and Britannia Rescue Stand. Additional spaces are available for the ambulant and visually impaired.
Helpers: Admitted
Prices: £15.00 – £30.00 for fans with disabilities. Helpers free
Disabled Toilets: Available in the each of the sections
Commentaries are available for the blind.
Contact: (01484) 960606 Option 5 (Bookings necessary)
Disability Liaison Officer – sue.farrell@htafc.com

Travelling Supporters' Information:
Routes: From the North, East and West: Exit the M62 at Junction 25 and take the A644 and A62 following Huddersfield signs. Follow signs for the Galpharm Stadium; From the South: Leave the M1 at Junction 38 and follow the A637/A642 to Huddersfield. At the Ring Road, follow signs for the A62 to the Galpharm Stadium.

HULL CITY AFC

Founded: 1904 (**Entered League**: 1905)
Nickname: 'Tigers'
Ground: KCom Stadium, West Park, Hull HU3 6HU
Ground Capacity: 25,586 (All seats)
Record Attendance: 25,030 (May 2010)
Pitch Size: 115 × 75 yards

Colours: Black and Amber shirts with Black shorts
Telephone Nº: (01482) 504600
Ticket Office: (01482) 358418
Fax Number: (01482) 304882
Web Site: www.hullcitytigers.com
E-mail: info@hulltigers.com

GENERAL INFORMATION

Car Parking: Walton Street Car Park (£5.00), City Centre Car Parks and a Park & Ride scheme from Priory Park (£1.20)
Coach Parking: By Police direction
Nearest Railway Station: Hull Paragon Interchange
Nearest Bus Station: City Centre, Hull
Club Shop: Tiger Leisure Superstore at the Stadium and in the Prospect Centre, Prince's Quay.
Opening Times: Superstore: Monday to Saturday 9.00am to 5.00pm and until 5.30pm on Saturday matchdays. Prospect Centre: Monday to Saturday 9.00am to 5.30pm and Sunday 10.30am to 4.30pm.
Telephone Nº: (01482) 504600 or (01482) 358362

GROUND INFORMATION

Away Supporters' Entrances & Sections:
North Stand

ADMISSION INFO (2019/2020 PRICES)

Ticket prices were not available at the time of going to press. Please contact the club for further information.

FANS WITH DISABILITIES INFORMATION

Wheelchairs: 131 spaces in total for Home and Away fans available around all the stands at both upper and lower level
Helpers: One helper admitted per fan with disabilities (subject to registration)
Prices: Normal prices for fans with disabilities. Helpers free.
Disabled Toilets: Available throughout the ground.
Lifts are available. Commentaries are available for the blind
Contact: (01482) 358303 (Bookings are not necessary)
Disability Liaison Officer – ann.holland@hulltigers.com

Travelling Supporters' Information:
Routes: From the West: Take the M62 then join the A63. Continue under the Humber Bridge as the road becomes the A63 Clive Sullivan Way and turn off at the slip road just before the flyover marked "Local Traffic/Infirmary". Take the 2nd exit at the roundabout into Rawling Way. Turn left at the next main set of traffic lights on A1105 Anlaby Road. Continue over the flyover then take a right turn into Walton Street. The car park is half way down this street after the Sports Arena; From the Humber Bridge: Follow signs for Hull City Centre – the road curves round to the left to join the A63 Clive Sullivan Way. Then as from the West; From the North: Take the A1079 towards Beverley then follow signs for the Humber Bridge and A164. Take the A63 sign-posted Hull City Centre and follow onto the A63 Clive Sullivan Way. Then as from the West.

IPSWICH TOWN FC

Founded: 1878 (**Entered League**: 1938)
Nickname: 'Town' 'Tractor Boys'
Ground: Portman Road, Ipswich IP1 2DA
Ground Capacity: 30,311 (All seats)
Record Attendance: 38,010 (8th March 1975)
Pitch Size: 110 × 72 yards

Colours: Blue shirts with White shorts
Telephone N°: (01473) 400500
Ticket Office: 03330 05 05 03
Fax Number: (01473) 400040
Web Site: www.itfc.co.uk
E-mail: enquiries@itfc.co.uk

GENERAL INFORMATION

Car Parking: Portman Road & Sir Alf Ramsey Way car parks
Coach Parking: Bibb Way
Nearest Railway Station: Ipswich (5 minutes walk)
Nearest Bus Station: Ipswich
Club Shop: Planet Blue Superstore at the ground
Opening Times: Weekdays 9.00am–5.00pm. Opening times on Matchdays vary. Please contact the club for details
Telephone N°: (01473) 400501

GROUND INFORMATION

Away Supporters' Entrances & Sections:
Cobbold Stand

ADMISSION INFO (2019/2020 PRICES)

Adult Seating: £23.00 – £47.00
Child Seating: £3.00 – £34.00
Senior Citizen Seating: £17.00 – £41.00
Note: Prices may be subject to change.
Programme Price: £3.00

FANS WITH DISABILITIES INFORMATION

Wheelchairs: 103 spaces and 103 seats for home fans in the East of England Cooperative, South and North Stands upper and lower tiers. 10 spaces and 10 seats for away fans in the lower East of England Cooperative Stand only.
Helpers: One helper admitted per fan with disabilities
Prices: Concessionary prices charged for each fan with disabilities plus one helper.
Disabled Toilets: Available around the ground
Commentaries are available for the blind
Contact: (01473) 400556 – lee.smith@itfc.co.uk
(Bookings are necessary)

Travelling Supporters' Information:
Routes: From the North and West: Take the A1214 from the A14/A12 following signs for Ipswich West only. Proceed through Holiday Inn Hotel traffic lights and at the 3rd set of traffic lights turn right into West End Road. The ground is ¼ mile along on the left; From the South: Follow signs for Ipswich West, then as from the North and West above.

LEEDS UNITED FC

Founded: 1919 (**Entered League**: 1920)
Former Names: Formed after Leeds City FC were wound up for 'Irregular Practices'
Nickname: 'United'
Ground: Elland Road, Leeds LS11 0ES
Ground Capacity: 39,460 (All seats)
Record Attendance: 57,892 (15th March 1967)

Pitch Size: 115 × 74 yards
Colours: White shirts and shorts
Telephone Nº: 0871 334-1919
Ticket Office: 0871 334-1992
Fax Number: (0113) 367-6050
Web Site: www.leedsunited.com
E-mail: reception@leedsunited.com

GENERAL INFORMATION

Car Parking: Large car parks adjacent to the Stadium
Coach Parking: Adjacent to the Stadium
Nearest Railway Station: Leeds City (1½ miles)
Nearest Bus Station: Leeds City Centre – specials from Swinegate
Club Shop: At the South East corner of the Stadium and also at the Merrion Shopping Centre in central Leeds.
Opening Times: At the ground: Monday to Saturday 9.00am to 5.30pm and Sunday 11.00am to 5.00pm. Also open for 1 hour after the final whistle on matchdays.
At the Merrion Centre: Weekdays 9.00am to 5.30pm and Sundays 11.00am to 5.00pm
Telephone Nº: 0871 334-1919 (Option 5)

GROUND INFORMATION

Away Supporters' Entrances & Sections:
South East Corner or South Stand – Upper & Lower Tiers

ADMISSION INFO (2019/2020 PRICES)

Adult Seating: £31.00 – £44.00
Concessionary Seating: £26.00 – £31.00
Under-16s Seating: £10.00 – £18.00
Under-11s Seating: £5.00 – £9.00 (Family Stand only)
Note: Prices vary according to the category of game played.

FANS WITH DISABILITIES INFORMATION

Wheelchairs: 131 spaces in total in special sections in the West, North, South and East Stands
Helpers: One helper admitted per fan with disabilities
Prices: Concessionary prices are charged
Disabled Toilets: Available around the ground
Commentaries via headphones in the West Stand
Contact: (0113) 367-6178 (Ms. Tracey Lazenby)
(Bookings are necessary)
E-mail: disabledinfo@leedsunited.com

Travelling Supporters' Information:
Routes: From the North: Take the A58 or A61 into the City Centre and follow signs to the M621. Leave the Motorway after 1½ miles and exit the roundabout onto the A643 into Elland Road; From the North-East: Take the A63 or A64 into the City Centre (then as from the North); From the South: Take the M1 to the M621 (then as from the North); From the West: Take the M62 to the M621 (then as from the North).

LEICESTER CITY FC

Founded: 1884 (**Entered League**: 1894)
Former Names: Leicester Fosse FC (1884-1919)
Nickname: 'Foxes'
Ground: King Power Stadium, Filbert Way, Leicester, LE2 7FL
Ground Capacity: 32,312 (All seats)
Record Attendance: 32,242 (August 2015)

Pitch Size: 110 × 72 yards
Colours: Blue shirts with White shorts
Telephone Nº: 0344 815-5000
Ticket Office: 0344 815-5000 (Option 1)
Fax Number: (0116) 229-4404
Web Site: www.lcfc.com
E-mail: lcfchelp@lcfc.co.uk

GENERAL INFORMATION

Car Parking: NCP Car Park (5 minutes walk). Also some pre-booked spaces at the ground may be available (£17.00)
Coach Parking: Sawday Street
Nearest Railway Station: Leicester (1 mile)
Nearest Bus Station: St. Margaret's (1 mile)
Club Shop: At the ground
Opening Times: Monday to Saturday 9.00am to 6.00pm. Saturday Matchdays open 9.00am until kick-off then for 30 minutes after the game. Sundays open 10.00am – 4.00pm
Telephone Nº: 0344 815-5000 Option 7

GROUND INFORMATION

Away Supporters' Entrances & Sections:
At the corner of the North and East Stands – Turnstiles 40-49

ADMISSION INFO (2019/2020 PRICES)

Adult Seating: £26.00 – £50.00
Under-22s Seating: £24.00 – £44.00
Under-18s Seating: £20.00 – £34.00
Under-16s Seating: £14.00 – £25.00
Under-12s Seating: £7.00 – £15.00
Under-10s Seating: £5.00 – £12.00
Senior Citizen Seating: £24.00 – £44.00
Note: Prices vary depending on the category of the game.
Programme Price: £3.00

FANS WITH DISABILITIES INFORMATION

Wheelchairs: 186 spaces for wheelchairs plus 111 spaces for helpers accommodated at various levels in all stands
Helpers: One carer admitted per fan with disabilities
Prices: Reduced prices are available – Phone for details
Disabled Toilets: Available in all stands
Contact: 0344 815-5000 Option 4 – disability@lcfc.co.uk
Liaison Officer: 07162 294544 (Jim Donnelly)

Travelling Supporters' Information:
Routes: From the North: Take the A46/A607 into the City Centre or exit the M1 at Junction 21, take the A5460, turn right ¾ mile after the Railway Bridge into Upperton Road, then right into Filbert Way; From the East: Take the A47 into the City Centre (then as from the North); From the South: Exit the M1 at Junction 21 and take the A5460, turn right ¾ mile after Railway Bridge into Upperton Road, then right into Filbert Way; From the West: Take the M69 to the City Centre (then as from North).

LEYTON ORIENT FC

Founded: 1881 (**Re-entered League**: 2019)
Former Names: Glyn Cricket and Football Club (1881-86); Eagle FC (1886-88); Clapton Orient FC (1888-1946); Leyton Orient FC (1946-66); Orient FC (1966-87)
Nickname: 'O's'
Ground: The Breyer Group Stadium, Brisbane Road, Leyton, London E10 5NF

Ground Capacity: 9,271 (all seats)
Record Attendance: 34,345 (21st January 1964)
Pitch Size: 110 × 76 yards
Telephone Nº: (020) 8926-1111
Ticket Office: (020) 8926-1010
Web Site: www.leytonorient.com
E-mail: info@leytonorient.net

GENERAL INFORMATION

Car Parking: Street parking
Coach Parking: By Police direction
Nearest Railway Station: Leyton Midland Road (½ mile)
Nearest Tube Station: Leyton (Central)
Club Shop: At the ground
Opening Times: Weekdays and Home Matchdays 10.00am to 3.00pm
Telephone Nº: (020) 8926-1009

GROUND INFORMATION

Away Supporters' Entrances & Sections: East Stand

ADMISSION INFO (2019/2020 PRICES)

Adult Seating: £20.00 – £32.00
Senior Citizen/Concessionary Seating: £18.00 – £29.00
Under-18s Seating: £7.00 – £29.00
Under-11s Seating: £3.00 – £29.00
Note: Tickets are cheaper when purchased in advance
Programme Price: £3.00

FANS WITH DISABILITIES INFORMATION

Wheelchairs: Spaces are available in the North, East and West Stands
Helpers: One helper admitted per fan with disabilities
Prices: Normal prices for fans with disabilities. Helpers free
Disabled Toilets: Available near the disabled sections
Contact: (020) 8926-1111 (Bookings are necessary)

Travelling Supporters' Information:
Routes: From the North & West: Take A406 North Circular, follow signs for Chelmsford to Edmonton. After 2½ miles take the 3rd exit at the roundabout towards Leyton (A112). Pass the railway station, turn right after ½ mile into Windsor Road and left into Brisbane Road; From the East: Follow the A12 to London then the City for Leytonstone. Follow Hackney signs into Grove Road, cross Main Road into Ruckholt Road then turn right into Leyton High Road, turn left after ¼ mile into Buckingham Road and left into Brisbane Road; From the South: Take the A102M through the Blackwall Tunnel, follow signs for Newmarket (A102) to join the A11 to Stratford, then follow signs for Stratford Station into Leyton Road to the railway station (then as from North).

LINCOLN CITY FC

Founded: 1884 (**Re-entered League**: 2017)
Nickname: 'Red Imps'
Ground: Sincil Bank Stadium, Lincoln LN5 8LD
Ground Capacity: 10,120 (All seats)
Record Attendance: 23,196 (15th November 1967)
Pitch Size: 110 × 72 yards

Colours: Red and White striped shirts, Black shorts
Telephone Nº: (01522) 880011
Ticket Office: (01522) 880011
Fax Number: (01522) 880020
Web Site: www.redimps.co.uk
E-mail: info@theredimps.com

GENERAL INFORMATION

Car Parking: No specific parking for visiting fans.
Street parking or the City Centre car parks are the only option.
Coach Parking: Please contact the club for details.
Nearest Railway Station: Lincoln Central
Club Shop: At the ground
Opening Times: Monday to Saturday 10.00am to 4.00pm and Saturday Matchdays 10.00am until kick-off and then after the final whistle until 5.30pm. Open from 10.00am until kick-off on midweek matchdays.
Telephone Nº: (01522) 539399

GROUND INFORMATION

Away Supporters' Entrances & Sections:
Stacey West Stand – Turnstiles 4 to 8

ADMISSION INFO (2019/2020 PRICES)

Adult Seating: £24.00 – £26.00
Junior/Junior Seating: £10.00 – £11.00
Concessionary Seating: £19.00 – £21.00
Note: Discounts are available for families and members.
Programme Price: £3.00

FANS WITH DISABILITIES INFORMATION

Wheelchairs: Limited number of spaces available in a special section adjacent to turnstile 23
Helpers: One helper admitted per fan with disabilities
Prices: Helpers are admitted free of charge if the supporter they are assisting is in receipt of the higher rate of disability allowance or enhanced PIP.
Disabled Toilets: Available
Contact: (01522) 880011 (Bookings are necessary)

Travelling Supporters' Information:
Routes: From the East: Take the A46 or A158 into the City Centre following Newark (A46) signs into the High Street and take next left (Scorer Street and Cross Street) for the ground; From the North and West: Take the A15 or A57 into the City Centre, then as from the East; From the South: Take the A1 then A46 for the City Centre, then into the High Street, parking on the South Common or in the Stadium via South Park Avenue, turn down by the Fire Station.

LIVERPOOL FC

Founded: 1892 (**Entered League**: 1893)
Nickname: 'Reds'
Ground: Anfield Road, Liverpool L4 0TH
Ground Capacity: 54,000 (All seats)
Record Attendance: 61,905 (2nd February 1952)
Pitch Size: 110 × 75 yards

Colours: Red shirts, shorts and socks
Telephone Nº: (0151) 264-2500
Ticket Office: 0843 170-5555
Ticket Office Fax Number: (0151) 261-1416
Web Site: www.liverpoolfc.com

GENERAL INFORMATION

Car Parking: None available in the immediate area
Coach Parking: Priory Road and Pinehurst Avenue
Nearest Railway Station: Kirkdale (¾ mile)
Nearest Bus Station: Paradise Street, Liverpool
Club Shop: At the ground, at Williamson Square and 'Liverpool One' in the City Centre, at 48 Eastgate Street, Chester CH1 1LE, at 9 Castle Lane, Belfast BT1 5DA and also at High Street, Birkenhead CH41 2RA
Opening Times: At Anfield, Williamson Square, Chester and Birkenhead: Monday to Saturday 9.00am to 5.30pm and Sunday 10.00am to 4.00pm (and until 5.00pm in Chester); At Liverpool One: Monday to Friday 9.30am to 8.00pm, Saturdays 9.00am – 7.00pm and Sundays 11.00am – 5.00pm; At Belfast: Monday to Saturday 9.30am to 6.00pm and Sunday 1.00pm to 5.00pm.
Telephone Nº: (0151) 264-2368 (Anfield store)

GROUND INFORMATION

Away Supporters' Entrances & Sections:
Anfield Road

ADMISSION INFO (2019/2020 PRICES)

Adult Seating: £37.00 – £59.00
Senior Citizen Seating: £28.00 – £44.00
Young Adult Seating: £18.50 – £29.50
Junior Seating: £9.00
Programme Price: £3.00

FANS WITH DISABILITIES INFORMATION

Wheelchairs: 263 spaces in total around the ground including 24 spaces for away fans in the Anfield Road Stand.
Helpers: One helper is admitted per wheelchair but a second helper can sometimes be accommodated
Prices: £14.00 to £44.00 for fans with disabilities, dependent on age. One helper is admitted free of charge with each fan with disabilities.
Disabled Toilets: Two available in the Paddock, two in the Kop Stand and one in the Anfield Road Stand
Commentaries are available for the visually impaired on request
Contact: (0151) 264-2500 Option 2 (Bookings are necessary)
E-mail: disability@liverpoolfc.com

Travelling Supporters' Information:
Routes: From the North: Exit the M6 at Junction 28 and follow Liverpool A580 signs into Walton Hall Avenue, pass Stanley Park and turn left into Anfield Road; From the South and East: Take the M62 to the end of the motorway, then turn right into Queen's Drive (A5058) and turn left after 3 miles into Utting Avenue. After 1 mile, turn right into Anfield Road; From North Wales: Take the Mersey Tunnel into the City Centre and follow signs for Preston (A580) into Walton Hall Avenue. Turn right into Anfield Road before Stanley Park.

LUTON TOWN FC

Founded: 1885 (**Re-entered League**: 2014)
Former Names: The club was formed by the amalgamation of Wanderers FC and Excelsior FC
Nickname: 'Hatters'
Ground: Kenilworth Road Stadium, 1 Maple Road, Luton LU4 8AW
Ground Capacity: 10,226 (All seats)
Record Attendance: 30,069 (4th March 1959)

Pitch Size: 110 × 72 yards
Colours: Orange shirts with Blue shorts
Telephone Nº: (01582) 411622
Ticket Office: (01582) 416976
Fax Number: (01582) 405070
Web Site: www.lutontown.co.uk
E-mail: info@lutontown.co.uk

GENERAL INFORMATION

Car Parking: Street parking
Coach Parking: Luton Bus Station
Nearest Railway Station: Luton (1 mile)
Nearest Bus Station: Bute Street, Luton
Club Shop: Kenilworth Road Forecourt and also at The Mall in Luton town centre
Opening Times: 10.00am to 5.00pm
Telephone Nº: (01582) 458368 (The Mall)

GROUND INFORMATION

Away Supporters' Entrances & Sections:
Oak Road for the Oak Stand

ADMISSION INFO (2019/2020 PRICES)

Adult Seating: £20.00 – £30.00
Under-10s Seating: £3.00 – £9.00
Under-17s Seating: £6.00 – £12.00
Under-19s Seating: £12.00 – £20.00
Under-22s Seating: £15.00 – £23.00
Senior Citizen Seating: £15.00 – £23.00
Over-75s Seating: £12.00 – £20.00
Note: Prices vary depending on the category of the game

FANS WITH DISABILITIES INFORMATION

Wheelchairs: 32 spaces in total for Home and Away fans in the disabled section, Kenilworth Road End and Main Stand
Helpers: One helper admitted per disabled person
Prices: Concessionary prices for the disabled. Helpers free
Disabled Toilets: Available adjacent to disabled area
Commentaries are available for the blind
Contact: (01582) 416976 (Bookings are necessary)

Travelling Supporters' Information:
Routes: From the North and West: Exit the M1 at Junction 11 and follow signs for Luton (A505) into Dunstable Road. Follow the one-way system and turn right back towards Dunstable, take the second left into Ash Road for the ground; From the South and East: Exit the M1 at Junction 10 (or A6/A612) into Luton Town Centre and follow signs into Dunstable Road. After the railway bridge, take the sixth turning on the left into Ash Road for the ground.

MACCLESFIELD TOWN FC

Founded: 1874
Former Names: Macclesfield FC
Nickname: 'The Silkmen'
Ground: Moss Rose Stadium, London Road, Macclesfield, Cheshire SK11 7SP
Ground Capacity: 6,335
Seating Capacity: 2,599
Record Attendance: 10,041 (1948)

Pitch Size: 105 × 66 yards
Colours: Blue shirts, White shorts and Blue socks
Telephone Nº: (01625) 264686
Ticket Office: (01625) 264686
Fax Number: (01625) 264692
Web Site: www.mtfc.co.uk
E-mail: reception@mtfc.co.uk

GENERAL INFORMATION

Car Parking: Ample parking available near the ground
Coach Parking: Near the ground
Nearest Railway Station: Macclesfield (1 mile)
Nearest Bus Station: Macclesfield
Club Shop: At the ground
Opening Times: Weekdays 9.30am to 5.00pm and Saturday matchdays 12.00pm to 3.00pm.
Telephone Nº: (01625) 264686

GROUND INFORMATION

Away Supporters' Entrances & Sections:
John Askey Terrace and the left side of the Moss Lane Stand

ADMISSION INFO (2019/2020 PRICES)

Adult Standing: £15.00
Adult Seating: £22.00
Senior Citizen Standing: £12.00
Senior Citizen Seating: £17.00
Under-25s Standing/Seating: £12.00
Under-18s/Student Standing/Seating: £6.00
Under-12s Standing/Seating: £3.00
Programme Price: £3.00

FANS WITH DISABILITIES INFORMATION

Wheelchairs: 45 spaces in front of the Estate Road Stand
Helpers: One helper admitted per fan with disabilities
Prices: Normal prices apply for fans with disabilities. Helpers are admitted free of charge
Disabled Toilets: 3 available
Contact: (01625) 264686 (Bookings are necessary)

Travelling Supporters' Information:
Routes: From the North: Exit the M6 at Junction 19 to Knutsford, follow the A537 to Macclesfield. Follow signs for the Town Centre, then for the A523 to Leek. The ground is 1 mile out of the Town Centre on the right; From the South: Exit the M6 at Junction 17 for Sandbach and follow the A534 to Congleton. Then take the A536 to Macclesfield. After passing The Rising Sun on the left, turn right into Moss Lane after approximately ¼ mile . Following this lane will take you to the ground.

MANCHESTER CITY FC

Founded: 1887 (**Entered League**: 1892)
Former Name: St.Mark's FC, Ardwick FC (1887-1894)
Nickname: 'Cityzens' 'City' 'Blues'
Ground: Etihad Stadium, Etihad Campus, Manchester M11 3FF
Ground Capacity: 55,097 (All seats)
Record Attendance: 54,693 (February 2016)

Pitch Size: 115 × 75 yards
Colours: Sky Blue shirtswith White shorts
Telephone N°: (0161) 444-1894 Option 5
Ticket Office: (0161) 444-1894 Options 1 or 2
Fax Number: (0161) 438-7999
Web Site: www.mancity.com
E-mail: mancity@mancity.com

GENERAL INFORMATION

Car Parking: 1,000 spaces available at the stadium. Another 7,000 spaces are available off site in the vicinity.
Coach Parking: Around 40 spaces available at the stadium
Nearest Railway Station: Ashburys (15 minutes walk) or Manchester Piccadilly (20 minutes walk)
Nearest Bus Station: 53, 54, 185, 186, 216, 217, 230, 231, 232, 233, 234, 235, 236, 237, X36 & X37 services stop at the stadium
Club Shop: At the stadium
Opening Times: Monday to Saturday 9.00am to 5.30pm, Sundays 11.00am to 5.00pm and before and after matches.
Telephone N°: (0161) 444-1894 Option 3

GROUND INFORMATION

Away Supporters' Entrances & Sections:
South Stand

ADMISSION INFO (2019/2020 PRICES)

Adult Seating: £31.50 – £76.50
Concessionary Seating: £24.50 – £60.50
Ages 18 to 21 Seating: £24.50 – £60.50
Junior Seating: £17.50 – £50.50
Programme Price: £3.00

FANS WITH DISABILITIES INFORMATION

Wheelchairs: 252 spaces available in total including 21 for away fans
Helpers: One helper admitted per disabled fan
Prices: Concessionary prices for the disabled. Helpers free
Disabled Toilets: 42 wheelchair accessible toilets are available around the stadium
Commentaries for the blind and lifts are also available
Contact: (0161) 444-1894 Option 4 (Bookings are recommended)

Travelling Supporters' Information:
Routes: From the North: Exit the M60 at Junction 23 onto the A635 then turn right onto the A662 Ashton New Road. The stadium is approximately 1½ miles on the right hand side; From the East: Exit the M60 at Junction 24 and follow the A57 into Manchester before turning right onto the A6010 for the stadium; From the South: Follow the A6 into Manchester and then turn right onto the A6010 for the stadium. Alternatively, exit the M60 at Junction 1 and follow the A34 Kingsway into Manchester before turning right onto the A6010 for the stadium; From the West: Take the M602 into Manchester and continue onto the A57 then the A57(M) Mancunian Way onto the A635. Follow the road right before turning left onto the A6010 for the stadium.

MANCHESTER UNITED FC

Founded: 1878 (**Entered League**: 1892)
Former Names: Newton Heath LYR FC (1878-1892), Newton Heath FC (1892-1902)
Nickname: 'Red Devils'
Ground: Sir Matt Busby Way, Old Trafford, Manchester M16 0RA
Ground Capacity: 74,994 (All seats)
Record Attendance: 76,962 (25th March 1939)

Pitch Size: 115 × 76 yards
Colours: Red shirts with White shorts
Telephone Nº: (0161) 868-8000 Option 4
Ticket Information: (0161) 868-8000 Option 1
Fax Number: (0161) 868-8804
Web Site: www.manutd.com
E-mail: enquiries@manutd.co.uk

GENERAL INFORMATION

Car Parking: Lancashire Cricket Ground and Car Park E3 on John Gilbert Way. Other approved car parks are signposted
Coach Parking: By Police direction
Nearest Railway Station: At the ground
Nearest Bus Station: Chorlton Street
Nearest Metro Station: Old Trafford (located at L.C.C.C.) and also Salford Quays
Club Shop: At the ground
Opening Times: Non-matchdays: Monday to Saturday 9.30am – 6.00pm and Sundays 11.00am to 5.00pm. Saturday Matchdays 9.00am to 5.30pm for early kick-offs, 9.30am to 6.00pm (3pm kick-off), 9.30am to 8.30pm (5.30pm kick-off) and 9.30am to 10.45pm (8.00pm kick-off). Sundays 10.30am – 4.30pm (1.30pm kick-off) and 10.00am to 4.00pm (4.00pm kick-off).
Magastore Telephone Nº: (0161) 868-8567
Museum & Tour Centre: (0161) 868-8000 (Option 3)

GROUND INFORMATION

Away Supporters' Entrances & Sections: Bobby Charlton (South) Stand (turnstile 22) & East Stand (turnstile 30)

ADMISSION INFO (2019/2020 PRICES)

Adult Seating: £36.00 – £58.00
Concessionary/Under-18s Seating: £22.00 – £28.00
Ages 18 to 20 Seating: £29.00 – £45.50
Under-16s Seating: £18.00
Programme Price: £3.00

FANS WITH DISABILITIES INFORMATION

Wheelchairs: 160 spaces in total for Home and Away fans in sections in the North East & North West quadrants
Helpers: One helper admitted per fan with disabilities
Prices: Concessionary prices charge for fans with disabilities. Helpers are admitted free of charge
Disabled Toilets: Available
Commentaries are available for the visually impaired
Contact: (0161) 868-8009 (Bookings are necessary)
E-mail: accessibility@manutd.co.uk

Travelling Supporters' Information:
Routes: From the North and West: Take the M61 to the M60 and exit at Junction 4 following Manchester (A5081) signs. Turn right after 2½ miles into Sir Matt Busby Way for the ground; From the South: Exit the M6 at Junction 19 and take Stockport (A556) road then Altrincham (A56). From Altrincham follow Manchester signs and turn left into Sir Matt Busby Way after 6 miles; From the East: Exit the M62 at Junction 17 and take the A56 to Manchester. Follow signs for the South then signs for Chester (Chester Road). Turn right into Sir Matt Busby Way after 2 miles.

MANSFIELD TOWN FC

Founded: 1897 (**Re-entered League**: 1892)
Former Name: Mansfield Wesleyans FC (1897-1905)
Nickname: 'Stags'
Ground: One Call Stadium, Quarry Lane, Mansfield, Nottinghamshire NG18 5DA
Ground Capacity: 10,000 (All seats)
Record Attendance: 24,467 (10th January 1953)
Pitch Size: 110 × 70 yards

Colours: Amber shirts with Royal Blue piping, Royal Blue shorts with Amber flash
Telephone Nº: (01623) 482482
Ticket Office: (01623) 482482
Fax Number: (01623) 482495
Web Site: www.mansfieldtown.net
E-mail: info@mansfieldtown.net

GENERAL INFORMATION

Car Parking: Large car park at the ground (£5.00)
Coach Parking: Adjacent to the ground
Nearest Railway Station: Mansfield (5 minutes walk)
Nearest Bus Station: Mansfield
Club Shop: In the South Stand of the Stadium
Opening Times: Weekdays 10.00am – 5.00pm and Matchdays 10.00am – 3.00pm
Telephone Nº: (01623) 482482

GROUND INFORMATION

Away Supporters' Entrances & Sections:
North Stand turnstiles for North Stand seating

ADMISSION INFO (2019/2020 PRICES)

Adult Seating: £24.50 – £25.50
Senior Citizen Seating: £20.50 – £21.50
Young Adult Seating: £18.50
Junior Seating: £14.50 – £16.50
Under-7s Seating: Free of charge
Note: There is a £2.00 discount for tickets bought in advance.

FANS WITH DISABILITIES INFORMATION

Wheelchairs: 90 spaces available in total in special sections in the North Stand, Quarry Street Stand and West Stand
Helpers: Admitted
Prices: Normal prices apply for the disabled. Free for helpers
Disabled Toilets: Available in the North Stand, West Stand and Quarry Lane Stand
Contact: (01623) 482482 (Please buy tickets in advance)

Travelling Supporters' Information:
Routes: From the North: Exit the M1 at Junction 29 and take the A617 to Mansfield. After 6¼ miles turn right at the Leisure Centre into Rosemary Street. Carry on to Quarry Lane and turn right; From the South and West: Exit the M1 at Junction 28 and take the A38 to Mansfield. After 6½ miles turn right at the crossroads into Belvedere Street then turn right after ¼ mile into Quarry Lane; From the East: Take the A617 to Rainworth, turn left at the crossroads after 3 miles into Windsor Road and turn right at the end into Nottingham Road, then left into Quarry Lane.

MIDDLESBROUGH FC

Founded: 1876 (**Entered League**: 1899)
Nickname: 'Boro'
Ground: Riverside Stadium, Middlesbrough, TS3 6RS
Ground Capacity: 33,742 (All seats)
Record Attendance: 34,836 (28th December 2004)
Pitch Size: 115 × 75 yards

Colours: Shirts are Red with White detailing, shorts are White
Telephone Nº: (01642) 929420
Ticket Office: (01642) 929421
Web Site: www.mfc.co.uk
E-mail: Contact the club via a form on the web site

GENERAL INFORMATION

Car Parking: 1,250 spaces available at the stadium – permit holders only. Otherwise use town centre parking.
Coach Parking: At the ground
Nearest Railway Station: Middlesbrough (½ mile)
Nearest Bus Station: Middlesbrough
Club Shops: At ground
Opening Times: Weekdays 9.00am to 5.00pm, Saturday Matchdays 9.00am to 3.00pm then 5.00pm to 6.00pm and Sundays 10.30am to 4.00pm.
Telephone Nº: (01642) 929422

GROUND INFORMATION

Away Supporters' Entrances & Sections:
East Stand

ADMISSION INFO (2019/2020 PRICES)

Adult Seating: £30.00 – £34.00
Senior Citizen Seating: £20.00 – £26.00
Under-18s Seating: £17.00
Note: Lower prices are available in the Family Zone and discounted prices are available for members.
Programme Price: £2.00

FANS WITH DISABILITIES INFORMATION

Wheelchairs: 2210 spaces available in total including 30 spaces for away fans in the East Stand
Helpers: One helper admitted per fan with disabilities
Prices: Normal prices for fans with disabilities. Helpers are admitted free of charge.
Disabled Toilets: Available in every stand with access via the Radar Key system
Contact: (01642) 757691 (Bookings are necessary)
E-mail contact: supporters@mfc.co.uk

Travelling Supporters' Information:
Routes: From the North: Take the A19 across the flyover and join the A66 (Eastbound). At the end of the flyover, turn left at North Ormesby where the ground is well-signposted. The ground is 200 metres down the road; From the South: Take the A1 and A19 to the junction with the A66 (Eastbound). After the flyover, turn left at North Ormesby following signs for the ground.

MILLWALL FC

Founded: 1885 (**Entered League**: 1920)
Former Names: Millwall Rovers FC (1885-1893); Millwall Athletic FC (1893-1925)
Nickname: 'The Lions'
Ground: The Den, Zampa Road, London SE16 3LN
Ground Capacity: 20,146 (All seats)
Record Attendance: 20,093 (10th January 1994)

Pitch Size: 116 × 74 yards
Colours: Dark Blue shirts with White shorts
Telephone Nº: (020) 7232-1222
Ticket Office: 0844 826-2004
Web Site: www.millwallfc.co.uk
E-mail: questions@millwallplc.com

GENERAL INFORMATION

Car Parking: Street parking
Coach Parking: Adjacent to the ground
Nearest Railway Station: New Cross Gate (1 mile) or South Bermondsey (½ mile)
Nearest Tube: New Cross Gate (1 mile)/Canada Water (1 mile)
Club Shop: Next to the Stadium
Opening Times: Daily from 9.30am to 5.00pm
Telephone Nº: (020) 7231-9845

GROUND INFORMATION

Away Supporters' Entrances & Sections:
North Stand turnstiles 31-36. A walkway from South Bermondsey Station to the ground is open on matchdays

ADMISSION INFO (2019/2020 PRICES)

Adult Seating: £20.00 – £32.00
Under-18s Seating: £11.00 – £18.00
Under-16s: £10.00 – £14.00 **Under-12s**: £5.00 – £9.00
Concessionary Seating: £14.00 – £22.00
Note: Prices vary depending on the category of the game
Programme Price: £3.00

FANS WITH DISABILITIES INFORMATION

Wheelchairs: 78 spaces in the West Stand and 17 spaces for away fans in front of the North Stand
Helpers: One helper admitted per wheelchair
Prices: Standard prices for fans with disabilities. Helpers free
Disabled Toilets: 17 toilets available around the Stadium
Commentaries are available for the blind
Contact: (020) 7232-1222 (Bookings are necessary)

Travelling Supporters' Information:
Routes: From the North: Follow City signs from the M1/A1 then signs for Shoreditch & Whitechapel. Follow Ring Road signs for Dover, cross over Tower Bridge and after 1 mile take 1st exit at the roundabout onto the A2. From Elephant and Castle take the A2 (New Kent Road) into Old Kent Road and turn left after 4 miles into Ilderton Road to Zampa Road; From the South: Take the A20 & A21 following signs to London. At New Cross follow signs for Surrey Quays into Kender Street, turn left into Old Kent Road then right into Ilderton Road. Zampa Road is the 7th turning on the right; From the East: Take the A2 to New Cross (then as from the South); From the West: From M4 & M3 follow the South Circular (A205) then follow signs for Clapham, the City (A3) then Camberwell to New Cross and then as from South.

MILTON KEYNES DONS FC

Founded: 2004
Former Names: None
Nickname: 'Dons'
Ground: Stadium MK, Stadium Way West, Milton Keynes MK1 1ST
Ground Capacity: 30,500 (All seats)
Record Attendance: 28,127 (vs Chelsea, 31/1/2016)

Pitch Size: 115 × 74 yards
Colours: White shirts and shorts
Telephone Nº: (01908) 622922
Ticket Office: 0333 200-5343
Fax Number: (01908) 622933
Web Site: www.mkdons.com
E-mail: info@mkdons.com

GENERAL INFORMATION

Car Parking: 1,600 Pay and Display spaces at Stadium MK (£7.00 charge). Disabled drivers can park free of charge on production of a valid blue badge (entry via Saxon Street).
Coach Parking: By Police direction
Nearest Railway Station: Bletchley (1 mile)
Nearest Bus Station: Bletchley
Club Shop: At the Stadium
Opening Times: Weekdays 9.00am to 5.00pm with extended hours on Matchdays
Telephone Nº: (01908) 622973

GROUND INFORMATION

Away Supporters' Entrances & Sections:
North Stand corner, Gate 3

ADMISSION INFO (2019/2020 PRICES)

Adult Seating: £22.00 – £32.00
Concessionary Seating: £17.00 – £27.00
Under-18s Seating: £7.00 – £17.00
Programme Price: £3.00

FANS WITH DISABILITIES INFORMATION

Wheelchairs: A total of 164 spaces are available around the ground at concourse level
Helpers: One helper admitted per fan with disabilities
Prices: Normal prices for fans with disabilities. Helpers are admitted free of charge
Disabled Toilets: Available
Contact: (01908) 622899 (Bookings are necessary) – disability@mkdons.com

Travelling Supporters' Information:
Routes: From all parts: Exit the M1 at Junction 14, following signs for Milton Keynes and cross the first roundabout onto H6 Childs Way. Turn left at the next roundabout onto V11 Tongwell Street. Continue along this road then turn right at the third roundabout onto H9 Groveway. Continue along Groveway then take the first exit at the fourth roundabout towards Central Bletchley. Stadium:MK is the first turning on the left.

MORECAMBE FC

Founded: 1920 (**Entered League**: 2007)
Former Names: None
Nickname: 'Shrimps'
Ground: Globe Arena, Christie Way, Westgate, Morecambe LA4 4TB
Record Attendance: 9,324 (1962 – Christie Park)
Pitch Size: 110 × 73 yards

Colours: Red shirts with Red shorts
Telephone Nº: (01524) 411797
Fax Number: (01524) 832230
Ground Capacity: 6,476
Seating Capacity: 2,247
Web site: www.morecambefc.com
E-mail: office@morecambefc.com

GENERAL INFORMATION

Car Parking: Available at a school adjacent to the ground
Coach Parking: Available at the rear of the stadium
Nearest Railway Station: Morecambe Central (2 miles)
Nearest Bus Station: Morecambe
Club Shop: At the ground
Opening Times: Weekdays & Matchdays 9.00am to 5.00pm
Telephone Nº: (01524) 411797 Option 3

GROUND INFORMATION

Away Supporters' Entrances & Sections:
Bay Radio (East) Away Stand plus seating in part of the Main Stand.

ADMISSION INFO (2019/2020 PRICES)

Adult Standing: £16.00 – £17.00
Adult Seating: £21.00 – £26.00
Senior Citizen Standing: £13.00 – £14.00
Senior Citizen Seating: £17.00 – £26.00
Ages 18 to 22 Standing: £10.00
Ages 18 to 22 Seating: £15.00 – £26.00
Ages 11 to 17 Standing: £5.00
Ages 11 to 17 Seating: £5.00 – £26.00
Note: Under-11s are admitted free with a paying adult. Otherwise, the same prices as Ages 11 to 17 are charged.
Programme Price: £3.00

FANS WITH DISABILITIES INFORMATION

Wheelchairs: Accommodated
Helpers: Admitted
Prices: Concessionary prices are charged for fans with disabilities. Helpers are admitted free of charge
Disabled Toilets: Available in all stands
Contact: (01524) 411797 (Bookings are preferred)

Travelling Supporters' Information:
Routes: Exit the M6 at Junction 34 and follow signs to Morecambe. Cross the River Lune via the Greyhound Bridge and continue, following signs for Morecambe onto the A589. At the first two roundabouts, keep in the right hand lane and carry straight on. Turn left at the third roundabout (Shrimp) and continue along Westgate for about a mile. Globe Stadium is on the right.
Away fans car parking: Turn right after the Junior School towards Venture Caravan Park and the away car park is signposted.

NEWCASTLE UNITED FC

Founded: 1882 (**Entered League**: 1893)
Former Names: Newcastle East End FC (1882-1892) amalgamated with Newcastle West End FC
Nickname: 'Magpies'
Ground: St. James Park, Strawberry Place, Newcastle-Upon-Tyne NE1 4ST
Ground Capacity: 52,305 (All seats)

Record Attendance: 68,386 (3rd September 1930)
Pitch Size: 115 × 74 yards
Colours: Black and White striped shirts, Black shorts
Telephone Nº: 0344 372-1892
Ticket Office: 0344 372-1892
Web Site: www.nufc.co.uk
E-mail: boxoffice@nufc.co.uk

GENERAL INFORMATION

Car Parking: Street parking
Coach Parking: By Police direction
Nearest Railway Station: Newcastle Central (¼ mile)
Nearest Bus Station: St. James' Boulevard (¼ mile)
Club Shop: At the ground
Opening Times: Monday to Saturday 9.00am – 5.00pm
Telephone Nº: 0344 372-1892

GROUND INFORMATION

Away Supporters' Entrances & Sections:
Rear of the Leazes Stand, entrance from Barrack Road

ADMISSION INFO (2019/2020 PRICES)

Adult Seating: £27.00 – £64.00
Child Seating: £14.00 – £34.00 (in the Family Seating Area)
Senior Citizen Seating: £22.00 – £52.00
Please contact the club for 2019/2020 pricing information.
Programme Price: £3.00

FANS WITH DISABILITIES INFORMATION

Wheelchairs: 234 spaces in total in special areas throughout the stadium
Helpers: One helper admitted per fan with disabilities
Prices: Half-price tickets for fans with disabilities. Helpers are admitted free of charge
Disabled Toilets: Throughout the stadium (via Radar Key)
Commentaries are available for 20 blind supporters
Contact: (0191) 201-8457 or disabilitysupport@nufc.co.uk

Travelling Supporters' Information:
Routes: From the North: Follow the A1 into Newcastle, then follow Hexham signs into Percy Street. Turn right into Leazes Park Road; From the South: Take the A1M, then after Birtley Granada Services take the A1 Gateshead Western Bypass (bear left on the Motorway). Follow Airport signs for approximately 3 miles then take the A692 (Newcastle) sign, crossing the Redheugh Bridge. Proceed over three sets of traffic lights to the roundabout and take the 1st exit into Barrack Road; From the West: Take the A69 towards the City Centre. Pass Newcastle General Hospital. At the traffic lights after the Hospital turn left into Brighton Grove. After 70 yards turn right into Stanhope Street and proceed into Barrack Road for the ground.

NEWPORT COUNTY AFC

Founded: 1989 (**Entered League**: 2013)
Former Names: Newport AFC
Nickname: 'The Exiles'
Ground: Rodney Parade, Newport NP19 0UU
Record Attendance: 9,836 (vs Tottenham Hotspur in January 2018 when temporary seating was erected)
Pitch Size: 112 × 72 yards

Colours: Amber shirts with Black shorts
Telephone N°: (01633) 415376
Ticket Office: (01633) 415374
Ground Capacity: 7,850
Seating Capacity: 1,236
Web site: www.newport-county.co.uk
E-mail: office@newport-county.co.uk

GENERAL INFORMATION

Car Parking: Street parking only
Coach Parking: By Police direction
Nearest Railway Station: Newport (½ mile)
Nearest Bus Station: Newport
Club Shop: At Kingsway Shopping Centre, Newport
Opening Times: Monday to Saturday 9.30am to 5.00pm (until 4.00pm on regular Saturdays). Saturday Matchdays 10.00am to 2.00pm.
Telephone N°: (01633) 481896

GROUND INFORMATION

Away Supporters' Entrances & Sections:
Sytner End turnstiles for Bisley Stand accommodation

ADMISSION INFO (2018/2019 PRICES)

Adult Standing: £19.00 **Adult Seating**: £21.00
Senior Citizen Standing/Seating: £17.00
Ages 16 to 21 Standing: £13.00 **Seating**: £15.00
Under-16s Standing/Seating: £9.00
Under-12s Standing/Seating: £7.00 (Under-6s free)
Note: Discounted prices are available for online purchases. Prices for the 2019/2020 season were not available at the time of going to press. Please contact the club for details.

FANS WITH DISABILITIES INFORMATION

Wheelchairs: Accommodated
Helpers: Admitted
Prices: Normal prices for fans with disabilities. Helpers free
Disabled Toilets: Available
Contact: (01633) 415376 (Bookings are not necessary)

Travelling Supporters' Information:
Routes: From the West: Exit the M4 at Junction 26 of the M4 and take the 3rd exit at the roundabout onto Malpas Road. Take the 2nd exit at the next roundabout then the 1st exit at the following roundabout across the River Usk bridge. * At the next set of traffic lights bear right onto Chepstow Road, take the first right onto Cedar Road then the first right onto Corporation Road. Take the next left onto Grafton Road and Rodney Parade is on left hand side; From The East: Exit the M4 at Junction 25A and take the 1st exit at the roundabout onto Heidenheim Way. Take the 1st exit off the fly-over then the 2nd exit at the first roundabout then the 1st exit at the next roundabout across the River Usk bridge. Then as above *.

NORTHAMPTON TOWN FC

Founded: 1897 (**Entered League**: 1920)
Nickname: 'Cobblers'
Ground: PTS Academy Stadium, Upton Way, Northampton NN5 5QA
Ground Capacity: 7,798 (All seats)
Record Attendance: 7,798 (September 2016)
Pitch Size: 116 × 72 yards

Colours: Claret and White shirts with White shorts
Telephone Nº: (01604) 683700
Ticket Office: (01604) 683777
Fax Number: (01604) 751613
Web Site: www.ntfc.co.uk

GENERAL INFORMATION

Car Parking: At the ground
Coach Parking: At the ground
Nearest Railway Station: Northampton Castle (2 miles)
Nearest Bus Station: North Gate
Club Shop: At the ground
Opening Times: Monday to Friday 9.00am – 5.00pm.. Saturday Matchdays 11.00am to 5.00pm and non-match Saturdays 9.00am to 12.00pm.
Telephone Nº: (01604) 683777

GROUND INFORMATION

Away Supporters' Entrances & Sections:
South Stand

ADMISSION INFO (2019/2020 PRICES)

Adult Seating: £24.00
Senior Citizen Seating: £20.00
Under-21s Seating: £18.00
Under-18s Seating: £12.00
Under-7s: Admitted free of charge
Note: Discounted prices are available for advance purchases

FANS WITH DISABILITIES INFORMATION

Wheelchairs: 80 spaces in total for Home and Away fans in various areas of the ground
Helpers: One helper admitted per fan with disabilities
Prices: Normal prices for fans with disabilities. Helpers free
Disabled Toilets: Available
Commentaries are available for the blind
Contact: (01604) 683777 (Bookings are necessary) – wendy.campbell@ntfc.co.uk (Supporters' Liaison Officer)

Travelling Supporters' Information:
Routes: From All Parts: Exit the M1 at Junction 15A following the signs for Sixfields Leisure onto Upton Way – the ground is approximately 2 miles.

NORWICH CITY FC

Founded: 1902 (**Entered League**: 1920)
Nickname: 'Canaries'
Ground: Carrow Road, Norwich NR1 1JE
Ground Capacity: 27,244 (All seats)
Record Attendance: 43,984 (30th March 1963)
Pitch Size: 114 × 74 yards

Colours: Yellow shirts with Green shorts
Telephone Nº: (01603) 760760
Ticket Office: (01603) 721902 Option 1
Fax Number: (01603) 613886
Web Site: www.canaries.co.uk
E-mail: reception@canaries.co.uk

GENERAL INFORMATION

Car Parking: City Centre car parks (nearby)
Coach Parking: Lower Clarence Road
Nearest Railway Station: Norwich Thorpe (1 mile)
Nearest Bus Station: Surrey Street, Norwich
Club Shop: At the ground and also stores in Chapelfield and the Castle Mall
Opening Times: Carrow Road store opens Monday to Saturday 9.00am to 5.30pm and Sunday 10.00am to 4.00pm. Chapelfield is open Monday to Saturday 9.00am to 6.00pm (until 8pm on Thursday and 7.00pm on Friday and Saturday), plus Sunday 11.00am to 5.00pm
Telephone Nº: (01603) 721902

GROUND INFORMATION

Away Supporters' Entrances & Sections:
South Stand using turnstiles 51-57

ADMISSION INFO (2019/2020 PRICES)

Adult Seating: £30.00
Senior Citizen Seating: £25.00
Under-18s Seating: £20.00
Under-12s Seating: £15.00
Programme Price: £3.00

FANS WITH DISABILITIES INFORMATION

Wheelchairs: 84 spaces for home fans and 13 for away fans in the South Stand. Plenty of spaces are also available for ambulant fans with disabilities
Helpers: One helper admitted per fan with disabilities
Prices: Normal prices for fans with disabilities. Helpers free
Disabled Toilets: Available – Radar key operated
Contact: (01603) 721902 (Bookings are necessary) – stephen.graham@canaries.co.uk (Supporters' Liaison Officer)

Travelling Supporters' Information:
Routes: From the South: Take the A11 or A140 and turn right onto the A47 towards Great Yarmouth & Lowestoft, take the A146 Norwich/Lowestoft sliproad, turn left towards Norwich and follow road signs for the Football Ground; From the West: Take the A47 on to the A146 Norwich/Lowestoft slip road. Turn left towards Norwich, follow the road signs for the Football Ground.

NOTTINGHAM FOREST FC

Founded: 1865 (**Entered League**: 1892)
Nickname: 'The Reds'
Ground: The City Ground, Nottingham NG2 5FJ
Ground Capacity: 30,445 (All seats)
Record Attendance: 49,946 (28th October 1967)
Pitch Size: 112 × 76 yards

Colours: Red shirts with White shorts
Telephone Nº: (0115) 982-4444
Ticket Office: (0115) 982-4388
Fax Number: (0115) 982-4455
Web Site: www.nottinghamforest.co.uk
E-mail: enquiries@nottinghamforest.co.uk

GENERAL INFORMATION

Car Parking: Various nearby car parks and street parking
Coach Parking: Available at the stadium.
Nearest Railway Station: Nottingham Midland (½ mile)
Nearest Bus Station: Victoria Street/Broadmarsh Centre
Club Shop: At the ground
Opening Times: Weekdays 9.00am – 5.00pm; Matchdays 9.00am – kick-off and 30 minutes after the game; Sunday matchdays 10.00am – kick-off + 60 minutes after the game
Telephone Nº: (0115) 982-4305

GROUND INFORMATION

Away Supporters' Entrances & Sections:
Entrances via East car park for Bridgford Stand

ADMISSION INFO (2019/2020 PRICES)

Due to the introduction of a 'dynamic' pricing system, we suggest that fans contact the club for further details about admission prices for any particular game.
Programme Price: £3.00

FANS WITH DISABILITIES INFORMATION

Wheelchairs: 68 spaces in total for home fans around the ground plus 11 spaces for away fans in the Lower Bridgford Stand
Helpers: One helper admitted per fan with disabilities
Prices: Please contact the club for further information
Disabled Toilets: 7 available with radar key locks
Contact: (0115) 982-4388 (Bookings are necessary)

Travelling Supporters' Information:
Routes: From the North: Exit the M1 at Junction 26 following Nottingham signs (A610) then signs to Melton Mowbray and Trent Bridge (A606). Cross the River Trent, turn left into Radcliffe Road then left again into Colwick Road for the ground; From the South: Exit the M1 at Junction 24 following signs for Nottingham (South) to Trent Bridge. Turn right into Radcliffe Road then left into Colwick Road; From the East: Take the A52 to West Bridgford and follow signs for Football & Cricket; From the West: Take the A52 into Nottingham, follow signs for Melton Mowbray and Trent Bridge, cross the River Trent (then as North).

OLDHAM ATHLETIC FC

Founded: 1895 (**Entered League**: 1907)
Former Names: Pine Villa FC (1895-1899)
Nickname: 'Latics'
Ground: Boundary Park, Furtherwood Road, Oldham OL1 2PA
Ground Capacity: 13,612 (All seats)
Record Attendance: 47,671 (25th January 1930)

Pitch Size: 110 × 72 yards
Colours: Blue shirts, shorts and socks
Telephone Nº: (0161) 624-4972
Ticket Office: (0161) 785-5150
Fax Number: (0161) 627-5915
Web Site: www.oldhamathletic.co.uk
E-mail: enquiries@oldhamathletic.co.uk

GENERAL INFORMATION

Car Parking: 350 spaces in North Stand car park (permit holders only) and also the nearby Hospital car park (£5.00)
Coach Parking: At the ground
Nearest Railway Station: Oldham Werneth (1½ miles)
Nearest Bus Station: Oldham Town Centre (2 miles)
Club Shop: In the North Stand
Opening Times: Daily from 9.00am to 6.00pm.
Telephone Nº: (0161) 624-4972

GROUND INFORMATION

Away Supporters' Entrances & Sections:
Chadderton Road Stand

ADMISSION INFO (2019/2020 PRICES)

Adult Seating: £22.00
Concessionary Seating: £10.00
Under-18s Seating: £7.00
Under-12s Seating: £5.00
Note: Discounts are available for tickets in the Family Stand in addition to those purchased in advance.
Programme Price: £3.00

FANS WITH DISABILITIES INFORMATION

Wheelchairs: 60 spaces in the special areas in the North Stand, Chadderton Road Stand and Rochdale Road Stand
Helpers: One helper admitted per fan with disabilities if on the higher/enhanced rate of care
Prices: Normal prices for fans with disabilities. Helpers free
Disabled Toilets: Available in the North Stand, Rochdale Road Stand and the Chadderton Road Stand
Contact: (0161) 785-5179 (Bookings are necessary)

Travelling Supporters' Information:
Routes: From All Parts: Exit the M62 at Junction 20 and take the A627M to the junction with the A664. Take the 1st exit at the roundabout onto Broadway, then the 1st right into Hilbre Avenue which leads to the car park at the ground.

OXFORD UNITED FC

Founded: 1893 (**Re-Entered League**: 2010)
Former Names: Headington United FC (1893-1960)
Nickname: 'U's'
Ground: Kassam Stadium, Grenoble Road, Oxford, OX4 4XP
Ground Capacity: 12,205 (All seats)
Record Attendance: 22,730 (At the Manor Ground)
Pitch Size: 110 × 70 yards
Colours: Yellow shirts with Navy Blue shorts
Telephone N°: (01865) 337500
Ticket Office: (01865) 337533
Web Site: www.oufc.co.uk

GENERAL INFORMATION

Car Parking: 2,000 free spaces available at the ground
Coach Parking: At the ground
Nearest Railway Station: Oxford (4 miles)
Nearest Bus Station: Oxford
Club Shop: At the ground and also in the Covered Market in Oxford city centre
Opening Times: Monday to Friday 10.00am to 5.00pm and Matchdays from 10.00am until kick-off at the ground. The Covered Market shop opens Tuesday to Friday 9.00am to 5.00pm and Saturday 10.00am to 4.00pm.
Telephone N°: (01865) 747231 (at the ground)

GROUND INFORMATION

Away Supporters' Entrances & Sections:
North Stand turnstiles for North Stand accommodation. Ticket office for away supporters is adjacent

ADMISSION INFO (2019/2020 PRICES)

Adult Seating: £20.00 – £28.00
Under-21s Seating: £14.00 – £20.00
Under-18s Seating: £8.00 – £18.00
Under-13s Seating: £6.00 – £15.00
Under-7s Seating: Free with a paying adult in the Family Area. Otherwise £4.00 – £12.00
Senior Citizen Seating: £13.00 – £21.00
Programme Price: £3.00

FANS WITH DISABILITIES INFORMATION

Wheelchairs: Accommodated in areas in the North, East and South Stands
Helpers: One assistant admitted per fan with disabilities
Prices: Normal prices for fans with disabilities. One assistant also admitted free of charge if required
Disabled Toilets: Available throughout the ground
Contact: (01865) 337533 (Bookings are not necessary)

Travelling Supporters' Information:
Routes: From the Oxford Ring Road take the A4074 towards Henley and Reading then turn left after ½ mile following signs for the Oxford Science Park. Bear left and go straight on at two roundabouts then the Stadium is on the left in Grenoble Road. The Kassam Stadium is clearly signposted on all major roads in Oxford.

PETERBOROUGH UNITED FC

Founded: 1934 (**Entered League**: 1960)
Nickname: 'Posh'
Ground: The Weston Homes Stadium, London Road, Peterborough PE2 8AL
Ground Capacity: 15,314
Seating Capacity: 10,000
Pitch Size: 112 × 71 yards

Record Attendance: 30,096 (20th February 1965)
Colours: Cobalt Blue shirts with Blue shorts
Telephone Nº: (01733) 563947
Ticket Office: 0844 847-1934
Fax Number: (01733) 344140
Web Site: www.theposh.com
E-mail: info@theposh.com

GENERAL INFORMATION

Car Parking: Adjacent to the ground at the Pleasure Fair Meadow council car park and the Railworld car park.
Coach Parking: In front of the (North) Main Stand
Nearest Railway Station: Peterborough (1 mile)
Nearest Bus Station: Peterborough (1 mile)
Club Shop: At the ground
Opening Times: Tuesday to Friday 9.00am to 5.00pm (from10.00am on Mondays). Saturday Matchdays 10.00pm to 3.00pm then 5.00pm to 5.30pm
Telephone Nº: (01733) 865668

GROUND INFORMATION

Away Supporters' Entrances & Sections:
Blocks 'A' and 'B' of the North Stand

ADMISSION INFO (2019/2020 PRICES)

Adult Standing: £22.00 – £24.00
Adult Seating: £26.00 – £28.00
Senior Citizen Standing: £17.00 – £19.00
Senior Citizen Seating: £21.00 – £23.00
Under-22s Standing: £13.00 – £15.00
Under-22s Seating: £17.00 – £19.00
Ages 12 to 17 Standing/Seating: £9.00 – £11.00
Under-12s Standing/Seating: £5.00
Note: Prices vary depending on the category of the game. Discounts are available for tickets purchased in advance
Programme Price: £3.00

FANS WITH DISABILITIES INFORMATION

Wheelchairs: 57 spaces available in total in the South Stand, North Stand and Motorpoint Stand
Helpers: One helper admitted per fan with disabilities
Prices: Normal prices for fans with disabilities. Helpers free
Disabled Toilets: Available in all areas of the ground
Contact: (01733) 865674 Option 2 (Bookings are necessary) Chris Abbott – fans@theposh.com

Travelling Supporters' Information:
Routes: From the North and West: Take the A1 then the A47 into the Town Centre and follow Whittlesey signs across the river into London Road; From the East: Take the A47 into the Town Centre (then as from the North); From the South: Take the A1 then the A15 into London Road.

PLYMOUTH ARGYLE FC

Founded: 1886 (**Entered League**: 1920)
Former Names: Argyle FC (1886-1903)
Nickname: 'Pilgrims' 'Argyle'
Ground: Home Park, Plymouth PL2 3DQ
Ground Capacity: 16,388 (All seats)
Record Attendance: 43,596 (10th October 1936)
Pitch Size: 112 × 73 yards

Colours: Green shirts and White shorts
Telephone Nº: (01752) 562561
Ticket Office: (01752) 907700
Fax Number: (01752) 606167
Web Site: www.pafc.co.uk
E-mail: argyle@pafc.co.uk

GENERAL INFORMATION

Car Parking: Car park for 1,000 cars is adjacent
Coach Parking: Central Park Car Park
Nearest Railway Station: Plymouth North Road
Nearest Bus Station: Coach hub off Mayflower Street
Club Shop: At the ground
Opening Times: Monday to Friday 9.00am to 5.00pm, Saturday home matchdays 9.00am to 3.00pm plus 30 minutes after the game. Saturday away matchdays 10.00am to 1.00pm.
Telephone Nº: (01752) 562561

GROUND INFORMATION

Away Supporters' Entrances & Sections:
Barn Park End turnstiles for Blocks 22/23 (covered seating)

ADMISSION INFO (2019/2020 PRICES)

Adult Seating: £23.00
Under-18s Seating: £10.00
Under-12s Seating: £6.00 **Under-8s Seating**: £4.00
Senior Citizen/Under-23s Seating: £18.00
Note: Tickets are cheaper if purchased before the matchday and Family Tickets are also available.
Programme Price: £3.00

FANS WITH DISABILITIES INFORMATION

Wheelchairs: 80 spaces Home fans and 28 spaces for Away fans at pitch level
Helpers: One helper admitted per fan with disabilities
Prices: Normal prices apply for fans with disabilities. Helpers are admitted free of charge
Disabled Toilets: Available throughout the stadium
Commentaries are available for the visually impaired
Contact: 0773 7002-262 nikki.francis@pafc.co.uk – Disability Liaison Officer (Bookings are necessary)

Travelling Supporters' Information:
Routes: From All Parts: Take the A38 to Tavistock Road (A386), then branch left following signs for Home Park (A386) and continue for 1¼ miles. The car park for the ground is on the left (signposted Home Park).

PORTSMOUTH FC

Founded: 1898 (**Entered League**: 1920)
Nickname: 'Pompey'
Ground: Fratton Park, 57 Frogmore Road, Portsmouth, Hants PO4 8RA
Ground Capacity: 18,931 (All seats)
Record Attendance: 51,385 (26th February 1949)
Pitch Size: 110 × 71 yards

Colours: Blue shirts with White shorts
Telephone Nº: 0345 646-1898
Ticket Office: 0345 646-1898
Fax Number: (023) 9273-4129
Web Site: www.portsmouthfc.co.uk
E-mail: info@pompeyfc.co.uk

GENERAL INFORMATION

Car Parking: Street parking plus a limited number of spaces at Fratton Park (first come, first served – £10.00 charge)
Coach Parking: By Police direction
Nearest Railway Station: Fratton (adjacent)
Nearest Bus Station: The Hard, Portsmouth
Club Shop: At the ground in Anson Road (North Stand)
Opening Times: Monday to Friday 9.00am – 5.30pm. Saturday and Weekday Matchdays 9.00am until half-time.

GROUND INFORMATION

Away Supporters' Entrances & Sections:
Apsley Road – Milton Road side for Apsley Road End

ADMISSION INFO (2019/2020 PRICES)

Adult Seating: £26.00
Junior Seating: £10.00 (£5.00 when accompanied)
Senior Citizen Seating: £20.00 (Ages 65+)
Ages 18 to 22 Seating: £18.00
Ages 2 to 17 Seating: £8.00
Note: Adults, Senior Citizens or Ages 17 to 22 must be accompanied by a Junior if they sit in the Family Section.
Programme Price: £3.00

FANS WITH DISABILITIES INFORMATION

Wheelchairs: 58 spaces available in total in a special section in the Fratton End including 5 spaces for away fans
Helpers: One helper admitted per fan with disabilities
Prices: Wheelchair users are charged £15.00 and ambulant fans with disabilities are charged £16.00. Free for helpers
Disabled Toilets: One available in disabled section (Radar Key required for access)
Contact: 0345 646-1898 (Bookings are necessary) – courtneyhollier@pompeyfc.co.uk (Disability Liaison Officer)

Travelling Supporters' Information:
Routes: From the North and West: Take the M27 and M275 to the end then take the 2nd exit at the roundabout and after ¼ mile turn right at the 'T' junction into London Road (A2047). After 1¼ miles cross the railway bridge and turn left into Goldsmith Avenue. After ½ mile turn left into Frogmore Road; From the East: Take the A27 following Southsea signs (A2030). Turn left at the roundabout (3 miles) onto the A288, then right into Priory Crescent and next right into Carisbrooke Road for the ground.

PORT VALE FC

Founded: 1876 (**Entered League**: 1892)
Former Names: Burslem Port Vale FC
Nickname: 'Valiants'
Ground: Vale Park, Hamil Road, Burslem, Stoke-on-Trent ST6 1AW
Ground Capacity: 19,148 (All seats)
Record Attendance: 49,768 (20nd February 1960)
Pitch Size: 114 × 77 yards

Colours: White shirts with a Black stripe, Shorts are Black with Amber trim
Telephone Nº: (01782) 655800
Ticket Office: (01782) 655821
Fax Number: (01782) 834981
Web Site: www.port-vale.co.uk
E-mail: enquiries@port-vale.co.uk

GENERAL INFORMATION

Car Parking: Car parks at the ground (£5.00)
Coach Parking: Hamil Road car park (£25.00)
Nearest Railway Station: Stoke
Nearest Bus Station: Burslem (adjacent)
Club Shop: At the ground
Opening Times: Monday to Friday 9.00am – 5.00pm and Saturday Matchdays 9.30am to 3.15pm
Telephone Nº: (01782) 655822

GROUND INFORMATION

Away Supporters' Entrances & Sections:
Hamil Road turnstiles, numbers 1 to 8

ADMISSION INFO (2019/2020 PRICES)

Adult Seating: £20.00 – £21.00
Ages 12 to 17 Seating: £8.00
Ages 18 to 21 Seating: £15.00 – £16.00
Under-12s Seating: Free of charge
Concessionary Seating: £15.00 – £16.00
Note: Discounted Family Tickets are available
Programme Price: £3.00

FANS WITH DISABILITIES INFORMATION

Wheelchairs: 46 spaces available in a special area in the Lorne Street/Bycars Corner
Helpers: One helper admitted per fan with disabilities
Prices: Normal prices for fans with disabilities. Helpers free
Disabled Toilets: Available
Commentaries are available – please contact the club
Contact: (01782) 655821 (Bookings are necessary) – janet.ellis@port-vale.co.uk (Disability Liaison Officer)

Travelling Supporters' Information:
Routes: From the North: Exit the M6 at Junction 16 and follow Stoke signs (A500). Branch left off the A500 at the exit signposted Tunstall and take the 2nd exit at the roundabout into Newcastle Street. Proceed through the traffic lights into Moorland Road and take the 2nd turning on the left into Hamil Road; From the South and West: Exit the M6 at Junction 15 and take the A5006 and A500. After 6¼ miles branch left (then as from the North); From the East: Take the A50 or A52 into Stoke following Burslem signs into Waterloo Road, turn right at Burslem crossroads into Moorland Road (then as from the North).

PRESTON NORTH END FC

Founded: 1880 (**Entered League**: 1888)
Nickname: 'Lilywhites' 'North End'
Ground: Deepdale, Sir Tom Finney Way, Preston, PR1 6RU
Ground Capacity: 23,404 (All seats)
Record Attendance: 42,684 (23rd April 1938)
Pitch Size: 109 × 73 yards (100 × 67 metres)

Colours: White shirts with Blue shorts
Telephone Nº: 0344 856-1964
Ticket Office: 0344 856-1966
Web Site: www.pnefc.net
E-mail: enquiries@pne.com

GENERAL INFORMATION

Car Parking: Four official car parks at the stadium plus further parking at Moor Park School
Coach Parking: By prior arrangement with the club
Nearest Railway Station: Preston (2 miles)
Nearest Bus Station: Preston (1 mile)
Club Shop: At the ground
Opening Times: Monday to Saturday 9.00am to 5.00pm and midweek matchdays 9.00am until kick-off
Telephone Nº: 0344 856-1965

GROUND INFORMATION

Away Supporters' Entrances & Sections:
Bill Shankly Kop

ADMISSION INFO (2019/2020 PRICES)

Adult Seating: £26.00 – £32.00
Age 19 to 24/Student/Apprentice Seating: £16.00 – £23.00
Ages 11 to 18 Seating: £9.00 – £10.00
Under-11s Seating: £2.00
Senior Citizen Seating: £18.00 – £25.00
Note: Discounted Family Tickets are also available
Programme Price: £3.00

FANS WITH DISABILITIES INFORMATION

Wheelchairs: Spaces are available for advance order
Helpers: One helper admitted per fan with disabilities
Prices: Normal prices for fans with disabilities. Helpers free
Disabled Toilets: Available throughout the ground
Commentaries are available for the blind
Contact: (01772) 693324 Hannah Woodburn (Disability Liaison Officer) (Bookings are usually necessary)

Travelling Supporters' Information:
Routes: From the North: Take the M6 then the M55 to Junction 1. Follow signs for Preston (A6). After 2 miles turn left at the crossroads into Blackpool Road (A5085). Turn right ¾ mile into Deepdale; From the South and East: Exit the M6 at Junction 31 and follow Preston signs (A59). Take the 2nd exit at the roundabout (1 mile) into Blackpool Road. Turn left after 1¼ miles into Deepdale; From the West: Exit the M55 at Junction 1 (then as from the North).

QUEEN'S PARK RANGERS FC

Founded: 1882 (**Entered League**: 1920)
Former Names: Formed by the amalgamation of St. Jude's FC and Christchurch Rangers FC
Nickname: 'Rangers' 'R's'
Ground: The Kiyan Prince Foundation Stadium, South Africa Road, London W12 7PJ
Ground Capacity: 18,181 (All seats)

Record Attendance: 35,353 (27th April 1974)
Pitch Size: 109 × 72 yards
Colours: Blue and White hooped shirts, White shorts
Telephone N°: (020) 8743-0262
Ticket Office: 08444 777007
Fax Number: (020) 8743-1158
Web Site: www.qpr.co.uk

GENERAL INFORMATION

Car Parking: Street parking
Coach Parking: By Police direction
Nearest Railway Station: Shepherd's Bush
Nearest Tube Station: White City (Central) or Wood Lane (Hammersmith & City)
Club Shop: Superstore at the ground
Opening Times: Weekdays 9.00am to 5.00pm. Weekday matchdays until 15 minutes before kick-off. Non-match Saturdays 9.00am to 5.00pm. Saturday matchdays 9.00am until 15 minutes before kick-off then 45 minutes after game (but not for evening matches)
Telephone N°: (020) 8749-6862

GROUND INFORMATION

Away Supporters' Entrances & Sections:
Access via South Africa Road turnstile 2 for School End Lower and Ellerslie Road turnstile 13 for School End Upper

ADMISSION INFO (2019/2020 PRICES)

Adult Seating: £19.00 – £39.00
Senior Citizen/Ages 18 to 21 Seating: £13.00 – £29.00
Under-18s Seating: £9.00 – £22.00
Under-8s Seating (Accompanied): Free – £19.00
Note: Prices shown are for matchday ticket purchases. Discounts are available to members and for advance purchases
Programme Price: £3.50

FANS WITH DISABILITIES INFORMATION

Wheelchairs: 24 spaces available
Helpers: One helper admitted per wheelchair
Prices: Concessionary prices for fans with disabilities. Free of charge for helpers
Disabled Toilets: Available
Commentaries for the blind are available in the Ellerslie Road Stand. Please contact the Ticket Office to arrange this facility.
Contact: (020) 8740-2502 (Bookings are necessary)

Travelling Supporters' Information:
Routes: From the North: Take M1 & M406 North Circular for Neasden, go left after ¾ mile (A404) following signs for Harlesden, Hammersmith, past White City Stadium, right into White City Road and left into South Africa Road; From the South: Take A206 then A3 across Putney Bridge and follow signs to Hammersmith then Oxford (A219) to Shepherd's Bush. Join the A4020 following signs to Acton, turn right (¼ mile) into Loftus Road; From the East: Take the A12, A406 then the A503 to join the Ring Road, follow Oxford signs and join the A40(M), branch left (2 miles) to the M41, take the 3rd exit at the roundabout to the A4020 (then as South); From the West: Take the M4 to Chiswick then the A315 & A402 to Shepherd's Bush, join A4020 (then as South).

READING FC

Founded: 1871 (**Entered League**: 1920)
Former Names: Formed by the amalgamation of Hornets FC (1877) and Earley FC (1889)
Nickname: 'Royals'
Ground: Madejski Stadium, Junction 11 M4, Reading, Berkshire RG2 0FL
Ground Capacity: 24,161 (All seats)
Record Attendance: 24,160 (vs Spurs, 2012)

Pitch Size: 114 × 74 yards
Colours: Blue and White hooped shirts, White shorts
Telephone N°: (0118) 968-1100
Ticket Office: (0118) 968-1313
Fax Number: (0118) 968-1101
Web Site: www.readingfc.co.uk
E-mail: supporterservices@readingfc.co.uk

GENERAL INFORMATION

Car Parking: 1,800 spaces available at the ground. Also another 2,000 spaces available nearby
Coach Parking: Please contact the club for details
Nearest Railway Station: Reading Central
Nearest Bus Station: Reading
Club Shop: At the ground
Opening Times: Monday to Saturday 9.00am – 5.30pm
Telephone N°: (0118) 968-1234

GROUND INFORMATION

Away Supporters' Entrances & Sections:
Turnstiles 9 and 10 for South Stand accommodation

ADMISSION INFO (2019/2020 PRICES)

Adult Seating: £23.00 – £29.00
Over-65s Seating: £16.00 – £20.00
Ages 18 to 24 Seating: £13.00 – £16.00
Under-18s Seating: £8.00 – £13.00
Under-13s Seating: £5.00 – £10.00
Note: Prices shown are for matchday ticket purchases. Discounts are available to members and for advance purchases
Programme Price: £3.00

FANS WITH DISABILITIES INFORMATION

Wheelchairs: A total of 128 spaces are available for wheelchairs throughout the stadium
Prices: Normal prices apply for fans with disabilities. Helpers are admitted free of charge
Disabled Toilets: Available
Commentaries for approximately 12 people are available
Contact: (0118) 968-1313 Option 2 – Paul Collins (Bookings necessary) **E-mail**: disability@readingfc.co.uk

Travelling Supporters' Information:
Routes: The stadium is situated just off Junction 11 of the M4 near Reading.

ROCHDALE AFC

Founded: 1907 (**Entered League**: 1921)
Former Names: Rochdale Town FC
Nickname: 'The Dale'
Ground: The Crown Oil Arena, Rochdale OL11 5DR
Ground Capacity: 10,249
Seating Capacity: 7,913
Record Attendance: 24,231 (10th December 1949)

Pitch Size: 114 × 76 yards
Colours: Blue and Black striped shirts with Blue shorts
Telephone Nº: (01706) 644648
Ticket Office: (01706) 644648 Option 8
Fax Number: (01706) 648466
Web Site: www.rochdaleafc.co.uk
E-mail: admin@rochdaleafc.co.uk

GENERAL INFORMATION

Car Parking: Street parking only
Coach Parking: By Police direction
Nearest Railway Station: Rochdale (2 miles)
Nearest Bus Station: Town Centre (1 mile)
Club Shop: At the ground
Opening Times: Weekdays 9.00am to 5.00pm, Saturday matchdays from 9.00am to 3.00pm then open again after the final whistle. Other Saturdays from 9.00am to 12.00pm
Telephone Nº: (01706) 644648 Option 3

GROUND INFORMATION

Away Supporters' Entrances & Sections:
Turnstiles 11 to 18 for Willbutts Lane

ADMISSION INFO (2019/2020 PRICES)

Adult Standing: £20.00
Adult Seating: £23.00 – £25.00
Ages 16 to 21/Senior Citizen Standing: £15.00
Ages 16 to 21/Senior Citizen Seating: £17.00 – £19.00
Under-16s Standing/Seating: £8.00
Note: Certain tickets are cheaper if purchased in advance.
Programme Price: £3.00

FANS WITH DISABILITIES INFORMATION

Wheelchairs: 33 spaces in total in special sections in the Main, Pearl Street and Willbutts Lane Stands
Helpers: One helper admitted per fan with disabilities
Prices: Concessionary prices are charged for wheelchair users. Ambulant fans with disabilities pay normal prices. Helpers are admitted free of charge
Disabled Toilets: Available
Contact: (01706) 644648 Option 8 (Bookings necessary)
gina.buckley@rochdaleafc.co.uk (Supporters' Liaison Officer)

Travelling Supporters' Information:
Routes: From All Parts: Exit the M62 at Junction 20 and take the A627(M) signposted Rochdale. At the end of this link road, filter left carry on for 400 yards and go straight on at the roundabout into Roche Valley Way signposted Spotland Stadium. At the traffic lights go staight ahead and the ground is on the right after ½ mile.

ROTHERHAM UNITED FC

Founded: 1870 (**Entered League**: 1893)
Former Names: Rotherham Town FC (1870-1896), Thornhill United FC (1884-1905) and Rotherham County FC (1905-1925)
Nickname: 'The Millers'
Ground: AESSEAL New York Stadium, New York Way, Rotherham S60 1AH
Ground Capacity: 12,000 (All seats)

Pitch Size: 110 × 72 yards
Record Attendance: 11,758 (7th September 2013)
Colours: Red shirts with White sleeves, White shorts
Telephone Nº: (01709) 827760
Ticket Office: (01709) 827768
Fax Number: (01709) 827774
Web Site: www.themillers.co.uk
E-mail: office@rotherhamunited.net

GENERAL INFORMATION

Car Parking: Street Parking and in Sheffield Road car parks
Coach Parking: By police direction
Nearest Railway Station: Rotherham Central (½ mile)
Nearest Bus Station: Rotherham Town Centre (½ mile)
Club Shop: At the ground
Opening Times: Weekdays 9.00am to 5.00pm, Saturdays 9.00am to 1.00pm (Matchdays until 30 minutes after kick-off)
Telephone Nº: 08444 140754

GROUND INFORMATION

Away Supporters' Entrances & Sections:
Meditemp Stand

ADMISSION INFO (2019/2020 PRICES)

Adult Seating: £25.00 – £29.00
Senior Citizen/Student Seating: £15.00 – £19.00
Ages 13 to 17 Seating: £9.00 – £11.00
Ages 8 to 12 Seating: £7.00 – £9.00
Under-8s Seating: £2.00 in the Family Stand
Programme Price: £3.00

FANS WITH DISABILITIES INFORMATION

Wheelchairs: Accommodated
Helpers: One helper admitted with each fan with disabilities
Prices: Supporters with disabilities are charged concessionary prices. Helpers are admitted free of charge
Disabled Toilets: Available
Contact: (01709) 827768 dlo@rotherhamunited.net (Bookings are necessary)

Travelling Supporters' Information:
Routes: From the North: Exit the M1 at Junction 34, follow Rotherham (A6109) signs to the traffic lights and turn right. The ground is ¼ mile on the right; From the South & West: Exit the M1 at Junction 33, turn right and follow signs for Rotherham. Turn left at the roundabout then right at the next roundabout. Follow the dual carriageway and continue straight on at the next roundabout. Turn left at the followingroundabout and the ground is on the left after ¼ mile; From the East: Take the A630 into Rotherham following Sheffield signs. Turn left at the 3rd roundabout (signposted Masborough) and the ground is on the right.

SALFORD CITY FC

Photo courtesy of John Mills @ Altius Photography

Founded: 1940
Former Names: Salford Central FC, Salford FC, Salford Amateurs FC plus some other early names
Nickname: 'The Ammies'
Ground: The Peninsula Stadium, Moor Lane, Salford, Manchester M7 3PZ
Record Attendance: 4,200 (vs 'Class of 92', 2017)

Colours: Red shirts with White shorts
Telephone Nº: (0161) 241-9772
Ground Capacity: 5,106
Seating Capacity: 2,246
Pitch Size: 110 × 70 yards
Web site: www.salfordcityfc.co.uk
E-mail: enquiries@salfordcityfc.co.uk

GENERAL INFORMATION

Car Parking: Street parking only
Coach Parking: At the ground
Nearest Railway Station: Clifton (2½ miles)
Club Shop: At the ground
Opening Times: Matchdays only
Telephone Nº: (0161) 241-9772

GROUND INFORMATION

Away Supporters' Entrances & Sections:
No usual segregation

ADMISSION INFO (2019/2020 PRICES)

Adult Standing: £10.00
Adult Seating: £10.00
Senior Citizen/Junior Standing: £5.00
Senior Citizen/Junior Seating: £5.00
Note: Under-5s are admitted free of charge when attending the game with a paying adult.

FANS WITH DISABILITIES INFORMATION

Wheelchairs: Accommodated
Helpers: Admitted
Prices: Normal prices are charged for fans with disabilities. Helpers are admitted free of charge
Disabled Toilets: Available in the club house
Contact: (0161) 241-9772 (Bookings are not necessary) – andy.giblin@salfordcityfc.co.uk (Secretary)

Travelling Supporters' Information:
Routes: Exit the M60 at Junction 17 and take the A56 Bury New Road towards Prestwich. Continue along, passing the A6044 (Hilton Lane) road then turn right along Moor Lane heading towards Kersal Moor and the Golf Course. The ground is on the left hand side of the road after a few hundred yards.

SCUNTHORPE UNITED FC

Founded: 1899 (**Entered League**: 1950)
Former Name: Scunthorpe and Lindsey United FC (1899-1912)
Nickname: 'The Iron'
Ground: Glanford Park, Jack Brownsword Way, Scunthorpe, North Lincolnshire DN15 8TD
Ground Capacity: 9,088
Seating Capacity: 6,322

Record Attendance: 9,077 (22nd September 2010)
Pitch Size: 112 × 72 yards
Colours: Blue shirt with Claret trim, Blue shorts
Telephone Nº: (01724) 840139
Ticket Office: (01724) 747670 (www.sufctickets.com)
Fax Number: (01724) 857986
Web Site: www.scunthorpe-united.co.uk
E-mail: receptionist@scunthorpe-united.co.uk

GENERAL INFORMATION

Car Parking: Spaces for 800 cars at the ground
Coach Parking: At the ground
Nearest Railway Station: Scunthorpe (1½ miles)
Nearest Bus Station: Scunthorpe (1½ miles)
Club Shop: At the ground
Opening Times: Weekdays 8.30am to 5.00pm
Matchdays 9.00am to 3.00pm and 4.45pm to 5.15pm
Telephone Nº: (01724) 849344

GROUND INFORMATION

Away Supporters' Entrances & Sections:
Turnstiles 6-7 for the South Stand (AMS Stand)

ADMISSION INFO (2019/2020 PRICES)

Adult Standing: £21.00 – £22.00
Adult Seating: £23.00 – £26.00
Concessionary Standing: £15.00 – £16.00
Concessionary Seating: £16.00 – £18.00
Under-18s Standing: £8.00 – £9.00 (Under-12s free)
Under-18s Seating: £6.00 – £9.00
Note: Discounted prices are available for members
Programme Price: £3.00

FANS WITH DISABILITIES INFORMATION

Wheelchairs: 10 spaces for Home fans and 6 spaces for Away fans in designated section of the Clugston Stand
Helpers: One helper admitted per fan with disabilities
Prices: Normal prices for fans with disabilities. One helper admitted free per fan requiring medium to higher rate of care.
Disabled Toilets: Available
Commentaries are available for the blind
Contact: (01724) 747670 (Bookings are necessary)

Travelling Supporters' Information:
Routes: From All Parts: Exit the M180 at Junction 3 onto the M181. Follow the M181 to the roundabout with the A18 and take the A18 towards Scunthorpe – the ground is on the right after 200 yards.

SHEFFIELD UNITED FC

Founded: 1889 (**Entered League**: 1892)
Nickname: 'Blades'
Ground: Bramall Lane, Sheffield S2 4SU
Ground Capacity: 32,609 (All seats)
Record Attendance: 68,287 (15th February 1936)
Pitch Size: 110 × 73 yards

Colours: Red and White striped shirts, Black shorts
Telephone Nº: (0114) 253-7200
Ticket Office: (0114) 253-7200
Web Site: www.sufc.co.uk
E-mail: info@sufc.co.uk

GENERAL INFORMATION

Car Parking: Street parking only
Coach Parking: By Police direction
Nearest Railway Station: Sheffield Midland (1 mile)
Nearest Bus Station: Pond Street, Sheffield (1 mile)
Club Shop: At the ground
Opening Times: Monday to Friday 9.00am to 5.00pm (until kick-off on matchdays). Saturdays 9.00am to 4.00pm (until 3.00pm and then for 30 minutes after the game on matchdays)
Telephone Nº: (0114) 253-7200

GROUND INFORMATION

Away Supporters' Entrances & Sections:
Redbrik – Bramall Lane Stand Lower Tier

ADMISSION INFO (2018/2019 PRICES)

Adult Seating: £25.00 – £37.00
Under-18s Seating: £12.00 – £20.00
Young Adult/Student Seating: £17.00 – £25.00
Senior Citizen Seating: £19.00 – £30.00
Note: Prices for the 2019/2020 season were not available at the time of going to press. Contact the club for information.
Programme Price: £3.00

FANS WITH DISABILITIES INFORMATION

Wheelchairs: 95 spaces available for home fans along with 10 spaces for away fans in the Westfield Corner Stand
Helpers: One helper admitted per wheelchair
Prices: Normal prices for fans with disabilities. Helpers free
Disabled Toilets: 12 available within the enclosure
Commentaries available for the blind on request
Contact: (0114) 253-7200 (Bookings are necessary) – kay.adkins@sufc.co.uk (Disability Liaison Officer)

Travelling Supporters' Information:
Routes: From the North: Exit the M1 at Junction 33 following signs to Sheffield (A57) and continue along Sheffield Parkway until the Park Square roundabout. Take the 3rd exit and follow the A61 (Sheffield). Midland Station is on the left, the road veers to the left then take the middle lane following the ring road to the right. Take the first exit at the roundabout into Bramhall Lane.; From the South: Exit the M1 at junction 29 and take the A617 (Chesterfield). Take the 3rd exit at the roundabout onto the A61 and continue to the Earl of Arundel and Surrey Public House. Turn left and continue into Bramhall Lane; From the East: Exit the M1 at Junctions 31 or 33 and take the A57 to the roundabout, take the 3rd exit into Sheaf Street (then as from the North); From the West: Take the A57 into Sheffield and take the 4th exit at the roundabout into Upper Hanover Street and at the 2nd roundabout take the 3rd exit into Bramall Lane.

SHEFFIELD WEDNESDAY FC

Founded: 1867 (**Entered League**: 1892)
Former Name: The Wednesday FC
Nickname: 'Owls'
Ground: Hillsborough, Sheffield S6 1SW
Ground Capacity: 34,835 (All seats)
Record Attendance: 72,841 (17th February 1934)

Pitch Size: 116 × 75 yards
Colours: Blue and White striped shirts, Black shorts
Telephone Nº: 03700 20-1867
Ticket Hotline: 03700 20-1867 Option 1
Web Site: www.swfc.co.uk
E-mail: mediaenquiries@swfc.co.uk

GENERAL INFORMATION

Car Parking: Street parking
Coach Parking: Clay Wheels Lane
Nearest Railway Station: Sheffield Midland (4 miles)
Nearest Bus Station: Pond Street, Sheffield (4 miles)
Club Shop: At the ground
Ground Opening Times: Monday to Friday from 9.00am to 5.00pm and non-match Saturdays from 9.00am to 12.00pm. Saturdays matchdays 9.00am to 3.00pm then 45 minutes after the game.
Telephone Nº: 03700 20-1867

GROUND INFORMATION

Away Supporters' Entrances & Sections:
Leppings Lane turnstiles for the West Stand, Upper Tier

ADMISSION INFO (2019/2020 PRICES)

Adult Seating: £25.00 – £49.00
Under-11s Seating: £10.00
Under-5s Seating: £5.00
Concessionary Seating: £15.00 – £39.00

FANS WITH DISABILITIES INFORMATION

Wheelchairs: 91 spaces for home fans and 9 spaces for visiting fans in special sections in the North Stand, Kop Stand and West Stand Lower. Ambulant fans with disabilities can sit in any section of the ground other than the Grandstand.
Helpers: Admitted
Prices: Normal prices for the disabled. Helpers free of charge
Disabled Toilets: Available in the North and West Stands
Commentaries are available for the blind
Contact: 03700 20-1867 Option 1 E-mail: dlo@sdwfc.co.uk
(Bookings are necessary)

Travelling Supporters' Information:
Routes: From the North, South and East: Exit the M1 at Junction 36 and follow signs to Sheffield (A61). Continue for 4 miles then take the 3rd exit at the 2nd roundabout into Leppings Lane. The ground is situated on the left; From the West: Take the A57 until the road splits in two. Take the left fork (A6101). After 3¾ miles turn left onto the one-way system and follow the road round to the right onto Holme Lane. This road becomes Bradfield Road. At the junction with the A61 (Penistone Road), turn left towards Barnsley. The stadium is on the left after Hillsborough Park.

SHREWSBURY TOWN FC

Founded: 1886 (**Entered League**: 1950)
Nickname: 'Salop' 'The Shrews' 'The Blues' 'Town'
Ground: Montgomery Waters Meadow, Oteley Road, Shrewsbury SY2 6ST
Ground Capacity: 9,875 (All seats)
Record Attendance: 18,917 (26th April 1961)
Pitch Size: 116 × 75 yards

Colours: Shirts and shorts are Blue and Amber
Telephone Nº: (01743) 289177
Ticket Office: (01743) 273943
Fax Number: (01743) 246942
Web Site: www.shrewsburytown.com
E-mail: info@shrewsburytown.co.uk

GENERAL INFORMATION

Car Parking: Limited parking at the stadium – Permit Holders only. Parking restrictions are imposed on matchdays with no parking allowed in the vicinity of the stadium. Visiting fans should use the Meole Brace Park & Ride Scheme – £2.00 per person for the return journey – see details below
Coach Parking: At the stadium
Nearest Railway Station: Shrewsbury (2½ miles)
Nearest Bus Station: Raven Meadows, Shrewsbury
Club Shop: At the ground
Opening Times: Monday to Friday 9.00am to 5.00pm. Saturday Matchdays 10.00am until kick-off.
Telephone Nº: (01743) 289177

GROUND INFORMATION

Away Supporters' Entrances & Sections: North Stand entrances and accommodation

ADMISSION INFO (2019/2020 PRICES)

Adult Seating: £20.00 – £22.00
Concessionary Seating: £15.00 – £17.00
Ages 12 to 18 Seating: £8.00 – £17.00
Ages 19 to 23/Student Seating: £15.00 – £17.00
Under-12s Seating: Free of charge
Note: Prices vary depending on the category of the game
Programme Price: £3.00

FANS WITH DISABILITIES INFORMATION

Wheelchairs: 85 spaces in the North, South and East Stands
Helpers: One helper admitted per fan with disabilities
Prices: £15.00 – £17.00 for fans with disabilities. Helpers are admitted free of charge
Disabled Toilets: 30 available throughout the ground
Contact: (01743) 289177 (Bookings are necessary) – lawrence.ellerby@shrewsburytown.co.uk

Travelling Supporters' Information:
Park & Ride information: Buses run every 15 minutes from 12.30pm to 2.30pm on Saturday matchdays and 6.15pm to 7.30pm on matchdays in the week. Parking is free and the return bus journey is £2.00 per person. Buses return to the car parks immediately after the match finishes and car parks will remain open for one hour only. Car Park Locations:
Oxon Park and Ride Site: From the West and North West. At the junction of the A5 and the A458 (Churncote Roundabout) follow the signs A458 'Shrewsbury Town Centre'. Oxon Park and Ride Site is clearly signposted; **The Shirehall**: From all routes proceed along the A5 to Emstrey Island Roundabout into Shrewsbury, take the A5064 along London Road to the Column roundabout. Take the 3rd exit at the roundabout and the first right into the Shirehall Car Park; **Shirehall Overflow Car Park**: Follow directions to London Road as above. Before you reach the roundabout the car park is on the right-hand side. Proceed on foot to the Shirehall main car park for the bus.

SOUTHAMPTON FC

Founded: 1885 (**Entered League**: 1920)
Former Names: Southampton St. Mary's YMCA FC (1885-1897)
Nickname: 'Saints'
Ground: St. Mary's Stadium, Britannia Road, Southampton SO14 5FP
Ground Capacity: 32,505 (All seats)
Record Attendance: 32,363 (28th April 2012)

Pitch Size: 112 × 72 yards
Colours: Red and White shirts with Black shorts
Telephone N°: 0845 688-9448
Ticket Office: 02381 780780
General Fax Number: 0845 688-9445
Web Site: www.southamptonfc.com
E-mail: sfc@saintsfc.co.uk

GENERAL INFORMATION

Car Parking: Park & Ride only – must be pre-booked
Coach Parking: By Police direction
Nearest Railway Station: Southampton Central
Nearest Bus Station: Western Esplanade
Club Shop: At the ground and also at West Quay
Opening Times: Monday to Friday 9.00am to 5.00pm and Saturdays 9.30am to 5.00pm
Telephone N°: 0845 688-9335 or 0845 688-9433

GROUND INFORMATION

Away Supporters' Entrances & Sections:
Northam Stand – Blocks 43 to 46

ADMISSION INFO (2019/2020 PRICES)

Adult Seating: £20.00 – £65.00
Senior Citizen Seating: £20.00 – £65.00
Ages 18 to 25 Seating: £15.00 – £65.00
Under-18s Seating: £10.00 – £65.00
Under-11s Seating: £5.00 – £65.00
Note: Prices vary depending on the category of the game
Programme Price: £3.00

FANS WITH DISABILITIES INFORMATION

Wheelchairs: 200 spaces in total for Home and Away fans throughout the ground
Helpers: One helper admitted per fan with disabilities
Prices: £20.00 – £40.00 (cheaper for seniors/younger fans)
Disabled Toilets: Available in all Stands – Radar key required
Contact: 02380 711980 (Bookings are necessary)
E-mail Contact: supporterrelations@saintsfc.co.uk

Travelling Supporters' Information:
Routes: Although the ground is situated in the Melbourne Street/Marine Parade area of Southampton, no parking is available in the immediate vicinity except by special arrangement for Disabled supporters. There are a number of well-signposted Park and Ride car parks around the City and those designated for Away fans should be clearly marked.

SOUTHEND UNITED FC

Founded: 1906 (**Entered League**: 1920)
Former Name: Southend Athletic FC
Nickname: 'Shrimpers' 'Blues'
Ground: Roots Hall Ground, Victoria Avenue, Southend-on-Sea SS2 6NQ
Ground Capacity: 12,055 (All seats)
Record Attendance: 31,033 (10th January 1979)

Pitch Size: 110 × 74 yards
Colours: Blue shirts and shorts
Telephone N°: (01702) 304050
Ticket Office: 08444 770077
Fax Number: (01702) 304124
Web Site: www.southendunited.co.uk
E-mail: info@southend-united.co.uk

GENERAL INFORMATION

Car Parking: Car park at the ground for 450 cars – Season Ticket holders only. Otherwise use street parking
Coach Parking: Car park at the ground. Coach drivers should contact the club prior to the game
Nearest Railway Station: Prittlewell (¼ mile)
Nearest Bus Station: London Road, Southend
Club Shop: At the ground
Opening Times: Monday to Friday and Matchdays 9.30am to 5.00pm. Non-Match Saturdays 10.00am to 3.00pm
Telephone N°: (01702) 351117

GROUND INFORMATION

Away Supporters' Entrances & Sections:
Turnstiles 13 to 16 for North Stand seating

ADMISSION INFO (2019/2020 PRICES)

Adult Seating: £25.00 (£22.00 purchased in advance)
Young Person/Student Seating: £17.00 (£14.00 advance)
Junior Seating (Under-17s): £12.00 (£10.00 in advance)
Under-9s Seating: £5.00 (£4.00 purchased in advance)
Senior Citizen Seating: £18.00 (£15.00 in advance)
Note: Tickets are cheaper when purchased in advance and other discounts are available in the Family Enclosure.
Programme Price: £3.00

FANS WITH DISABILITIES INFORMATION

Wheelchairs: 20 spaces in total for Home and Away fans in a special section in the West Stand
Helpers: One helper admitted per fan with disabilities
Prices: Concessionary prices apply for fans with disabilities. Helpers receive complimentary tickets
Disabled Toilets: Available – Radar key required
Commentaries are available for the blind
Contact: 08444 770077 (Bookings are necessary)
or e-mail tickets@southend-united.co.uk

Travelling Supporters' Information:
Routes: From the North and West: From the M25 take Junction 29 and follow the A127 to Southend. About 1 mile outside of Southend Town Centre, take the 3rd exit at the roundabout into Victoria Avenue for the ground; From the A13: Follow signs for Southend, turn left into West Road at Westcliff. At the end of West Road turn left into Victoria Avenue – the ground is on the left.

STEVENAGE FC

Founded: 1976
Former Names: None
Nickname: 'Boro'
Ground: Lamex Stadium, Broadhall Way, Stevenage, Hertfordshire SG2 8RH
Record Attendance: 8,040 (25th January 1998)
Pitch Size: 110 × 70 yards

Colours: Red and White shirts with Red shorts
Telephone N°: (01438) 223223
Ground Capacity: 6,025
Seating Capacity: 3,404
Web site: www.stevenagefc.com
E-mail: info@stevenagefc.com

GENERAL INFORMATION

Car Parking: Fairlands Show Ground (opposite)
Coach Parking: None at the Stadium
Nearest Railway Station: Stevenage (1 mile)
Nearest Bus Station: Stevenage
Club Shop: At the ground
Opening Times: Thursday and Friday 10.00am to 7.00pm, Tuesday and Saturday Matchdays from 12.00pm to kick-off then for 15 minutes after the game.
Telephone N°: (01438) 223223

GROUND INFORMATION

Away Supporters' Entrances & Sections:
South Stand entrances and accommodation

ADMISSION INFO (2019/2020 PRICES)

Adult Standing: £20.00
Adult Seating: £24.00
Under-18s Standing: £12.00
Under-18s Seating: £16.00
Under-12s Standing: £5.00
Under-12s Seating: £10.00
Concessionary Standing: £17.00
Concessionary Seating: £22.00
Programme Price: £3.00

FANS WITH DISABILITIES INFORMATION

Wheelchairs: 13 spaces available by the North Terrace
Helpers: Admitted
Prices: Concessionary prices apply for fans with disabilities. Free of charge for helpers
Disabled Toilets: Yes
Contact: (01438) 218072 (Lindsay Powell) – dslo@stevenagefc.com (Bookings are necessary)

Travelling Supporters' Information:
Routes: Exit the A1(M) at Junction 7 and take the B197. The ground is on the right at the 2nd roundabout.
Bus Routes: SB4 and SB5

STOKE CITY FC

Founded: 1863 (**Entered League**: 1888)
Former Name: Stoke FC
Nickname: 'The Potters'
Ground: bet365 Stadium, Stanley Matthews Way, Stoke-on-Trent ST4 4EG
Ground Capacity: 30,089 (All seats)
Record Attendance: 30,022 (17th March 2018)

Pitch Size: 115 × 74 yards
Colours: Red and White striped shirts, White shorts
Telephone Nº: (01782) 367598
Ticket Office: (01782) 367599
Fax Number: (01782) 592210
Web Site: www.stokecityfc.com
E-mail: info@stokecityfc.com

GENERAL INFORMATION

Car Parking: At the ground (bookings necessary). Also various car parks within 10 minutes walk
Coach Parking: At the ground
Nearest Railway Station: Stoke-on-Trent (1½ miles)
Nearest Bus Station: Glebe Street, Stoke-on-Trent
Club Shop: At the ground and at the Potteries Shopping Centre in Hanley
Opening Times: Weekdays 9.00am–5.30pm, non-match Saturdays 9.00am–2.00pm. Weekend Matchdays 9.00am to kick-off then 30 minutes after the final whistle. Evening games 9.00am to kick-off and 30 minutes after the game. Potteries Store: Monday to Saturday 9.00am–6.00pm (until 8.00pm on Thursday) and Sunday 10.30am to 4.30pm.
Telephone Nº: (01782) 592242 (shop at the ground) and (01782) 592132 (Potteries shop)

GROUND INFORMATION

Away Supporters' Sections: South Stand

ADMISSION INFO (2019/2020 PRICES)

Adult Seating: £25.00 – £50.00
Under-17s Seating: £15.00 – £27.00
Under-11s Seating: £8.00 – £24.00
Senior Citizen Seating: £19.00 – £35.00
Note: Prices vary depending on the category of the game
Programme Price: £3.50

FANS WITH DISABILITIES INFORMATION

Wheelchairs: 186 spaces available in total
Helpers: One helper admitted per disabled person
Prices: £19.00 to £35.00 for each disabled fan plus helper
Disabled Toilets: Available
Commentaries are available – phone for details
Contact: (01782) 367599 (Bookings are necessary) or e-mail accessibility@stokecityfc.com

Travelling Supporters' Information:
Routes: From the North, South and West: Exit the M6 at Junction 15 and take the A500 to Stoke-on-Trent then the A50 towards Derby/Uttoxeter (the bet365 Stadium is signposted and visible to the right). Once on the A50 take the fist exit, turn right at the traffic lights and cross over the flyover. Turn right at the first roundabout, left at the next roundabout and right at the third roundabout for the stadium; From the East: Take the A50 to Stoke-on-Trent and take the last turn-off (signposted for bet365 Stadium). Go straight on at the first roundabout then right at the second roundabout to reach the stadium.

SUNDERLAND AFC

Founded: 1879 (**Entered League**: 1890)
Former Names: Sunderland and District Teachers FC
Nickname: 'The Black Cats'
Ground: Stadium of Light, Sunderland SR5 1SU
Ground Capacity: 49,000 (All seats)
Record Attendance: 48,335 (13th April 2002)
Pitch Size: 110 × 74 yards (101 × 68 metres)

Colours: Red and White striped shirts, Black shorts
Telephone Nº: 0371 911-1200
Ticket Office: 0371 911-1973
Fax Number: (0191) 551-5123
Web Site: www.safc.com
E-mail: enquiries@safc.com

GENERAL INFORMATION

Car Parking: Spaces for 1,100 cars (reserved)
Coach Parking: At the ground
Nearest Railway Station: Sunderland (1 mile)
Nearest Bus Station: Town Centre (1 mile)
Club Shop: At the Stadium, plus smaller stores at Debenhams in Sunderland
Opening Times: Monday to Saturday 9.00am – 5.30pm and Sunday 10.00am to 4.00pm
Telephone Nº: (0191) 551-5375

GROUND INFORMATION

Away Supporters' Entrances & Sections:
South Stand

ADMISSION INFO (2018/2019 PRICES)

Adult Seating: £18.00 – £45.00
Senior Citizen Seating: £15.00 – £45.00
Under-22s Seating: £10.00 – £45.00
Under-16s Seating: £7.50 – £45.00
Note: Prices for the 2019/2020 season were not available at the time of going to press. Please contact the club for details.
Programme Price: £3.00

FANS WITH DISABILITIES INFORMATION

Wheelchairs: 202 spaces in total throughout the stadium
Helpers: Admitted
Prices: Normal prices for fans with disabilities. Helpers free
Disabled Toilets: Available in all stands and Corporate areas
Contact: 0371 911-1200 (Bookings are necessary) – chris.waters@safc.com (Disability Liaison Officer)

Travelling Supporters' Information:
Routes: From All Parts: Exit the A1 at the A690 Durham/Sunderland exit. After approximately 4 miles turn left onto the A19 (signposted Tyne Tunnel). Keep in the left lane and take the slip road (signposted Washington/Sunderland) onto the bridge over the River Wear. Turn right onto the A1231 (signposted Washington/Sunderland), stay on this road going straight across 4 roundabouts into Sunderland. Continue straight through 2 sets of traffic lights and the Stadium car park is on the right, about 1 mile past the traffic lights.

SWANSEA CITY FC

Founded: 1912 (**Entered League**: 1920)
Former Name: Swansea Town FC (1912-1970)
Nickname: 'The Swans'
Ground: Liberty Stadium, Landore, Swansea, SA1 2FA
Ground Capacity: 21,000 (All seats)
Record Attendance: 32,796 (at the Vetch Field)

Pitch Size: 115 × 74 yards
Colours: White and Black shirts, shorts and socks
Telephone Nº: (01792) 616400
Ticket Office: (01792) 616400 Option 1
Fax Number: (01792) 616606
Web Site: www.swanseacity.com
E-mail: info@swanseacityfc.co.uk

GENERAL INFORMATION

Car Parking: Reserved parking only at the stadium but 3,000 spaces are available in a Park & Ride scheme just off Junction 45 of the M4.
Coach Parking: By Police direction
Nearest Railway Station: Swansea High Street (1½ miles)
Nearest Bus Station: Quadrant Depot (2½ miles)
Club Shop: At the ground
Opening Times: Monday to Friday 10.00am to 5.00pm, Saturday from 9.00am to 5.00pm and Sunday 10.00am to 4.00pm
Telephone Nº: (01792) 616400

GROUND INFORMATION

Away Supporters' Entrances & Sections:
North Stand

ADMISSION INFO (2019/2020 PRICES)

Adult Seating: £25.00 – £30.00
Concessionary Seating: £15.00 – £17.50
Under-18s Seating: £10.00 – £15.00
Under-12s Seating: £5.00
Note: A £2.50 ticket booking fee applies (£1.25 online). Discounted prices are available for members.
Programme Price: £3.00

FANS WITH DISABILITIES INFORMATION

Wheelchairs: 250 spaces available in total for Home and Away fans together with 250 spaces for helpers
Helpers: One helper admitted per wheelchair
Prices: Normal prices apply for fans with disabilities. Free of charge for helpers
Disabled Toilets: Available
There are a number of disabled parking spaces available at the stadium
Contact: (01792) 616600 (Bookings are necessary) or e-mail accessibility@swanseacity.com (Mark Phillips)

Travelling Supporters' Information:
Routes: From All Parts: Exit the M4 at Junction 45 and follow signs for Swansea (A4067). The stadium is clearly signposted.

SWINDON TOWN FC

Founded: 1881 (**Entered League**: 1920)
Nickname: 'Robins'
Ground: The Energy Check County Ground, County Road, Swindon SN1 2ED
Ground Capacity: 15,728 (All seats)
Record Attendance: 32,000 (15th January 1972)
Pitch Size: 110 × 70 yards

Colours: Red shirts and shorts
Telephone Nº: 0330 002-1879
Ticket Office: 0330 002-1879
Web Site: www.swindontownfc.co.uk

GENERAL INFORMATION

Car Parking: Town Centre
Coach Parking: Car park adjacent to the ground
Nearest Railway Station: Swindon (½ mile)
Nearest Bus Station: Swindon (½ mile)
Club Shop: The Swindon Town Superstore
Opening Times: Weekdays 9.00am – 5.00pm, Non-Matchday Saturdays 9.00am – 12.00pm and Saturday Matchdays 9.00am to 6.00pm
Telephone Nº: 0330 002-1879

GROUND INFORMATION

Away Supporters' Entrances & Sections:
Arkell's Stand turnstiles for the Stratton Bank

ADMISSION INFO (2019/2020 PRICES)

Adult Seating: £19.00 – £23.00
Concessionary Seating: £15.00 – £17.00
Under-21s Seating: £10.00
Under-18s Seating: £6.00
Under-11s Seating: £2.00
Note: A selection of family tickets are also available
Programme Price: £3.00

FANS WITH DISABILITIES INFORMATION

Wheelchairs: 61 spaces in total for Home and Away fans in a special section in front of Arkell's Stand
Helpers: One helper admitted with each fan in a wheelchair
Prices: Concessionary prices for fans with disabilities. Helpers are admitted free of charge.
Disabled Toilets: Available
Commentaries are available for the blind
Contact: 0330 002-1879 (Bookings are necessary) – markisaacs@swindontownafc.co.uk (Disability Liaison)

Travelling Supporters' Information:
Routes: From London, the East and the South: Exit the M4 at Junction 15 and take the A345 into Swindon along Queen's Drive. Take the 3rd exit at 'Magic Roundabout' into County Road; From the West: Exit the M4 at Junction 15 then as above; From the North: Take the M4 or A345/A420/A361 to the County Road roundabout, then as above.

TOTTENHAM HOTSPUR FC

Founded: 1882 (**Entered League**: 1908)
Former Name: Hotspur FC (1882-1884)
Nickname: 'Spurs'
Ground: Tottenham Hotspur Stadium, White Hart Lane, Bill Nicholson Way, 782 High Road, Tottenham, London N17 0BX
Ground Capacity: 62,062 (All seats)

Colours: White shirts with Navy Blue shorts
Telephone N°: 0344 499-5000
Ticket Office: 0344 844-0102
Fax Number: 0344 844-0102
Web Site: www.tottenhamhotspur.com
E-mail: supporter.services@tottenhamhotspur.com

GENERAL INFORMATION

Car Parking: None within ¼ mile of the ground
Coach Parking: Northumberland Park, West Road
Nearest Railway Station: White Hart Lane (nearby) or Northumberland Park
Nearest Tube Station: Seven Sisters (Victoria Line) or Manor House (Piccadilly Line)
Club Shop: At the stadium and in Chelmsford, Harlow and Stevenage
Opening Times: Varies from store to store. Stadium store opening times are Monday to Saturday 10.00am – 5.00pm and Sunday 10.30am – 4.30pm. For matches which finish after 5.00pm the store will remain open for 30 minutes after the final whistle. For 12.30pm kick-offs, it will open at 9.00am.
Telephone N°: 0344 499-5000 or (020) 8365-5042

GROUND INFORMATION

Away Supporters' Entrances & Sections:
North east corner of the stadium

ADMISSION INFO (2019/2020 PRICES)

Adult Seating: £30.00 – £98.00
Senior Citizen Seating: £15.00 – £35.00
Under-22s Seating: £22.50 – £52.50
Under-18s Seating: £15.00 – £35.00

FANS WITH DISABILITIES INFORMATION

Wheelchairs: 265 spaces available in total around the stadium
Helpers: Please contact the club for details
Prices: Please contact the club for pricing information
Disabled Toilets: 66 available throughout the stadium
Contact: (020) 8365-5161 (Bookings are necessary) or e-mail access@tottenhamhotspur.com

Travelling Supporters' Information:
Routes: From All Parts: Take the A406 North Circular to Edmonton and at traffic lights follow signs for Tottenham (A1010) into Fore Street for the ground.

TRANMERE ROVERS FC

Founded: 1884
Former Name: Belmont FC
Nickname: 'Rovers' 'Super White Army'
Ground: Prenton Park, Prenton Road West, Birkenhead CH42 9PY
Ground Capacity: 16,582 (All seats)
Record Attendance: 24,424 (5th February 1972)

Pitch Size: 110 × 70 yards
Colours: White shirts with Blue shorts
Telephone N°: 03330 144452
Ticket Office: 03330 144452 Option 2
Fax Number: (0151) 609-0606
Web Site: www.tranmererovers.co.uk
E-mail: customerservice@tranmererovers.co.uk

GENERAL INFORMATION

Car Parking: Large car park at the ground (£5.00 per car)
Coach Parking: At the ground (£10.00 charge)
Nearest Railway Stations: Hamilton Square, Rock Ferry and Conway Park (approximately 1½ miles)
Nearest Bus Station: Conway Park (Town Centre)
Club Shop: At the ground
Opening Times: Weekdays 9.00am–5.00pm, Saturday Matchdays 10.00am until kick-off, non-Saturday matchdays 10.00am–1.00pm and Sundays 11.00am to 4.00pm
Telephone N°: 03330 144452 Option 1

GROUND INFORMATION

Away Supporters' Entrances & Sections:
Summit Marine Scaffolding Cowshed Stand turnstiles 5-9 – access from Borough Road (Away section capacity: 2,500)

ADMISSION INFO (2019/2020 PRICES)

Adult Seating: £20.00 – £25.00
Under-12s Seating: £2.00 – £5.00
Under-18s Seating: £7.00 – £10.00
Senior Citizen Seating: £13.00 – £18.00
Young Persons Ticket (Ages 18-22): £13.00 – £18.00
Programme Price: £3.00
Note: Discounted prices are available for advance purchases. Under-12s must be accompanied by an adult.

FANS WITH DISABILITIES INFORMATION

Wheelchairs: 54 spaces in total for Home and Away fans in the disabled section, Bebington Paddock
Helpers: One helper admitted per fan with disabilities
Prices: £13.00 – £18.00 for fans with disabilities (with a free ticket for a carer)
Disabled Toilets: 2 available in the disabled section
Contact: (0151) 609-3380 (Bookings are necessary) – christiner@tranmererovers.co.uk (Disability Liaison Officer)

Travelling Supporters' Information:
Routes: From the North: From Liverpool city centre, travel through the Kingsway (Wallasey) Mersey Tunnel (£1.70 toll for cars) then continue onto the M53, exiting at Junction 3. Take the first exit (signposted Birkenhead), continue past Sainsbury's then turn right at the traffic lights by the Halfway House pub then turn left into Prenton Road West at the next set of lights. The ground is on the right after a short distance. From the South: Exit the M53 at Junction 4 and take the 4th exit at the roundabout onto the B5151 Mount Road (the ground is signposted from here). After 2½ miles, turn right at the traffic lights (by the United Reformed Church) into Prenton Road West for the ground.

WALSALL FC

Founded: 1888 (**Entered League**: 1892)
Former Name: Walsall Town Swifts FC (1888-1895)
Nickname: 'Saddlers'
Ground: Banks's Stadium, Bescot Crescent, Walsall, West Midlands WS1 4SA
Ground Capacity: 11,300 (All seats)
Record Attendance: 11,049 (9th May 2004)
Pitch Size: 110 × 73 yards

Colours: Red shirts with White shorts
Telephone Nº: (01922) 622791
Ticket Office: (01922) 651416 or (01922) 651414
Fax Number: (01922) 613202
Web Site: www.saddlers.co.uk
E-mail: info@walsallfc.co.uk

GENERAL INFORMATION

Car Parking: Car park at the ground
Coach Parking: At the ground
Nearest Railway Station: Bescot (adjacent)
Nearest Bus Station: Bradford Place, Walsall
Club Shop: At the ground
Opening Times: Weekdays 9.00am – 4.30pm and Saturday Matchdays 10.00am to 5.30pm
Telephone Nº: (01922) 651405

GROUND INFORMATION

Away Supporters' Entrances & Sections:
Turnstiles 21-28 for the University of Wolverhampton Stand

ADMISSION INFO (2019/2020 PRICES)

Adult Seating: £20.00 – £22.00
Child Seating: £11.00 – £13.00
Concessionary Seating: £16.00 – £18.00
Note: Discounts are available for advance bookings and savings from Family Tickets are available in some stands
Programme Price: £3.00

FANS WITH DISABILITIES INFORMATION

Wheelchairs: 36 spaces in total for Home and Away fans in the a special section in the St. Francis Group Community Stand
Helpers: One helper admitted with each fan with disabilities
Prices: Normal prices apply for fans with disabilities. Helpers are admitted free of charge
Disabled Toilets: Available
A special Lounge for fans with disabilities is available
Contact: (01922) 651416 (Bookings are necessary) or e-mail disabled@walsallfc.co.uk

Travelling Supporters' Information:
Routes: From All Parts: Exit the M6 at Junction 9 turning North towards Walsall onto the A461. After ¼ mile turn right into Wallows Lane and pass over the railway bridge. Then take the 1st right into Bescot Crescent and the ground is ½ mile along on the left adjacent to Bescot Railway Station.

WATFORD FC

Founded: 1881 (**Entered League**: 1920)
Former Names: Formed by the amalgamation of West Herts FC and St. Mary's FC
Nickname: 'Hornets'
Ground: Vicarage Road Stadium, Watford, WD18 0ER
Ground Capacity: 21,438 (All seats)
Record Attendance: 34,099 (3rd February 1969)

Pitch Size: 114 × 73 yards
Colours: Yellow & Black striped shirts, Black shorts
Telephone N°: (01923) 496000
Ticket Office: (01923) 223023
Fax Number: (01923) 496001
Web Site: www.watfordfc.com
E-mail: yourvoice@watfordfc.com

GENERAL INFORMATION

Car Parking: Nearby multi-storey car parks and schools
Coach Parking: By Police direction
Nearest Railway Station: Watford Junction or Watford Tube Station (Metropolitan Line)
Nearest Bus Station: Watford Town Centre
Club Shop: The Hornets Shop at Vicarage Road Stadium
Opening Times: Monday to Saturday 9.30am to 6.00pm
Telephone N°: (01923) 496000

GROUND INFORMATION

Away Supporters' Entrances & Sections:
Vicarage Road End entrances and accommodation

ADMISSION INFO (2019/2020 PRICES)

Adult Seating: £30.00 – £42.00
Under-16s Seating: £5.00 – £20.00
Student Seating: £18.00 – £24.00
Senior Citizen Seating: £22.00 – £28.00
Programme Price: £3.50

FANS WITH DISABILITIES INFORMATION

Wheelchairs: 151 spaces in total in accessible platforms located in all 4 stands.
Prices and Helpers: Normal prices for fans with disabilities. One assistant is admitted free with each fan with disabilities
Disabled Toilets: Available
Commentaries available around the ground – no charge
Contact: (01923) 223023 (Bookings in advance helpful) or e-mail disabled.supporters@watfordfc.com

Travelling Supporters' Information:
Routes: Vicarage Road is closed to traffic from 2 hours before kick-off on matchday. The following directions lead to the nearest car park: From the North and East: Exit the M25 at Junction 20 and take the first exit onto the A41. At the next roundabout, take the second exit onto A411 (Hempstead Road).* Continue along the A411 to the town centre. At the large roundabout take the second exit feeding into the inner ring road, which is a one-way system. Stay in the righthand lane and follow the Ring Road until you see the entrance to the Church car park on your right hand side; From the South and West: Exit the M25 at Junction 19 then take the third exit at the roundabout onto A411 (Hempstead Road). Then as from * above; From Central London: Exit the M1 Junction 5 and take the second exit onto the A4008. Cross the first roundabout, then take the second exit at the next towards the town centre. At the traffic lights, turn left onto the inner ring road at the T-junction and filter across to the right-hand lane. Follow the Ring Road until you see the entrance to the Church car park on your right hand side.

WEST BROMWICH ALBION FC

Founded: 1879 (**Entered League**: 1888)
Former Name: West Bromwich Strollers (1879-1880)
Nickname: 'Throstles' 'Baggies' 'Albion'
Ground: The Hawthorns, Halfords Lane,
West Bromwich, West Midlands B71 4LF
Ground Capacity: 26,850 (All seats)
Record Attendance: 64,815 (6th March 1937)

Pitch Size: 115 × 74 yards
Colours: Navy Blue & White striped shirts, White shorts
Telephone Nº: 0871 271-1100
Ticket Office: (0121) 227-2227
Fax Number: 0871 271-9861
Web Site: www.wba.co.uk
E-mail: enquiries@wbafc.co.uk

GENERAL INFORMATION

Car Parking: Halfords Lane Car Parks, East Stand Car Park and several independent car parks
Coach Parking: At the ground
Nearest Railway Station: Hawthorns (200 yards) or Rolfe Street, Smethwick (1½ miles)
Nearest Midland Metro: Hawthorns (200 yards)
Nearest Bus Station: West Bromwich Town Centre
Club Shop: At the ground and at the Merry Hill Centre
Opening Times: Weekdays 9.00am – 5.00pm, Saturday Matchdays 9.00am – 2.45pm and Sundays 10.00am – 2.00pm
Telephone Nº: (0121) 524-3473 (Stadium Megastore), 0871 271-9793 (Merry Hill Centre)

GROUND INFORMATION

Away Supporters' Entrances & Sections:
Smethwick End 'A' turnstiles

ADMISSION INFO (2019/2020 PRICES)

Adult Seating: £20.00 – £23.00
Concessionary Seating: £15.00 – £17.00
Under-23s/Student Seating: £15.00
Under-18s Seating: £10.00
Under-11s Seating: £5.00
Programme Price: £3.00

FANS WITH DISABILITIES INFORMATION

Wheelchairs: 171 spaces in total in special sections in the Birmingham Road End, Smethwick End and East Stand
Helpers: One helper admitted with each fan with disabilities (subject to availability of space)
Prices: £10.00 – £15.00 for fans with disabilities. Helpers free
Disabled Toilets: 14 in total available around the ground
Contact: (0121) 227-2227 (Bookings are necessary) – liz.marsey@wbafc.co.uk (Disability Liaison Officer)

Travelling Supporters' Information:
Routes: From All Parts: Exit the M5 at Junction 1 and follow Matchday signs for the ground. The matchday traffic plan has made the "obvious" route via the A41 unusable for home games.

WEST HAM UNITED FC

Photograph courtesy of Queen Elizabeth Olympic Park

Founded: 1895 (**Entered League**: 1919)
Former Name: Thames Ironworks FC
Nickname: 'Hammers'
Ground: London Stadium, Queen Elizabeth Olympic Park, Marsh Gate Lane, London E20 2ST
Ground Capacity: 60,000 (All seats)
Record Attendance: 59,988 (vs Everton 30/3/2019)

Pitch Size: 115 × 74 yards
Colours: Claret and Blue shirts with White shorts
Telephone Nº: (020) 8548-2748
Ticket Office: 03330 301966
Web Site: www.whufc.com
E-mail: supporterservices@westhamunited.co.uk

GENERAL INFORMATION

Car Parking: Limited spaces available at the Olympic Park. See Travelling Supporters' Information below for more details
Nearest Railway Station: Stratford (20 minutes walk)
Nearest Tube Station: Stratford (20 minutes walk)
Club Shops: At the Stadium and also at Lakeside Thurrock, Liberty Romford and Basildon
Opening Times: Vary by store. Stadium opening hours are Monday to Saturday 9.30am to 5.00pm (from 9.00am on Saturdays) and Sunday 11.00am to 5.00pm.
Telephone Nº: (01708) 890258 (Lakeside Store) or (01708) 741877 (Liberty Romford)

GROUND INFORMATION

Away Supporters' Entrances & Sections:
South West corner of the stadium – Block D

ADMISSION INFO (2019/2020 PRICES)

Adult Seating: £30.00 – £80.00
Senior Citizen Seating: £18.00 – £80.00
Under-21s Seating: £18.00 – £80.00
Under-16s Seating: £18.00 – £80.00
Programme Price: £3.50

FANS WITH DISABILITIES INFORMATION

Wheelchairs: 253 spaces available throughout the stadium including 24 for away fans
Helpers: Admitted
Prices: Concessionary prices apply for fans with disabilities. Free of charge for helpers
Disabled Toilets: 49 available in all areas of the stadium
Contact: 03330 300174 (Bookings are necessary) or accessibility@westhamunited.co.uk (Julie Pidgeon)

Travelling Supporters' Information:
Routes: Due to the fact that there is restricted car parking in the area of the stadium, it is recommended that visitors use the many public transport links available nearby, with tube and rail links plus numerous bus and coach routes close to the stadium. For those who choose to travel by car, the stadium is located in the Stratford area of east London, just to the east of the A12 and to the north of the River Thames. Visitors travelling by car are advised to use the public car parks at the Westfield Stratford City shopping centre, Stratford International station and the Stratford Centre.

WIGAN ATHLETIC FC

Founded: 1932 (**Entered League**: 1978)
Nickname: 'Latics'
Ground: DW Stadium, Loire Drive, Wigan, Lancashire WN5 0UZ
Ground Capacity: 25,146 (All seats)
Record Attendance: 25,133 (11th May 2008)
Pitch Size: 115 × 74 yards

Colours: Blue and White striped shirts, Blue shorts
Telephone Nº: (01942) 774000
Ticket Office: (01942) 311111
Fax Number: (01942) 770444
Web Site: www.wiganathletic.com
E-mail: feedback@wiganathletic.com

GENERAL INFORMATION

Car Parking: 2,500 spaces available at the ground (£5.00 for cars, £10.00 for minibuses, £20.00 for coaches)
Coach Parking: At the ground
Nearest Railway Station: Wallgate and Wigan North Western (1 mile)
Nearest Bus Station: Wigan
Club Shop: At the Stadium (matchdays only from 3 hours before kick-off) plus the Grand Arcade Shopping Centre.
Opening Times: Monday to Saturday 9.00am to 5.30pm, Sundays and Bank Holidays 10.30am – 4.30pm
Telephone Nº: (01942) 248413 or 239655 (Grand Arcade)

GROUND INFORMATION

Away Supporters' Entrances & Sections: North Stand

ADMISSION INFO (2019/2020 PRICES)

Adult Seating: £20.00 – £30.00
Senior Citizen Seating: £15.00
Under-18s Seating: £10.00
Under-12s Seating: £5.00
Under-5s Seating: £2.00
Programme Price: £3.00

FANS WITH DISABILITIES INFORMATION

Wheelchairs: 156 spaces available in total
Helpers: One helper admitted with each fan with disabilities
Prices: Normal prices for fans with disabilities. Helpers free
Disabled Toilets: 20 available in total
Contact: (01942) 311111 (Bookings are necessary) – l.peet@dwstadium.com (Disability Liaison Officer)

Travelling Supporters' Information:
Routes: From North: Exit M6 at Junction 27, turn left at end of slip road then right at T-junction, signposted Shevington. After 1 mile turn left at the mini-roundabout into Old Lane (B5375). After approx. 2 miles winding through countryside turn right at traffic lights into Scot Lane. Stadium is next left; From South & West: Exit M6 at Junction 25 follow signs for Wigan (A49). After approx. 2 miles a complex junction is reached, keep in left-hand lane (McDonalds on right). Turn left at traffic light filter lane into Robin Park Road. Turn right at third set of traffic lights and follow road to stadium; From East: Exit M61 Junction 6, take 1st exit at roundabout. At next roundabout take 1st left into Chorley Road. Follow signs for Wigan B5238, first turning right then left at Aspull Roundabout. After 2 miles turn right at traffic lights after Earl of Balcarres Pub to face Tesco. Turn left at lights, keep in left lane turn left at next lights with the Quality Hotel on the corner. Follow ring road, get into second lane from right as road bears right into Caroline Street, signposted Orrell. Continue on ring road as it bears left passing B&Q on left, pass Wigan Pier on right and as road goes under railway bridge get into right hand lane to turn right at lights into Robin Park Road. Then South & West.

WOLVERHAMPTON WANDERERS FC

Founded: 1877 (**Entered League**: 1888)
Former Names: Formed by the amalgamation of St. Luke's FC and The Wanderers Football & Cricket Club in 1879. St. Luke's is considered the start of the club
Nickname: 'Wolves'
Ground: Molineux Stadium, Waterloo Road, Wolverhampton WV1 4QR
Ground Capacity: 31,700

Record Attendance: 61,305 (11th February 1939)
Pitch Size: 110 × 75 yards
Colours: Gold shirts with Black shorts
Telephone N°: 0371 222-2220
Ticket Office: 0371 222-1877
Fax Number: (01902) 687006
Web Site: www.wolves.co.uk
E-mail: info@wolves.co.uk

GENERAL INFORMATION

Car Parking: Around West Park, Newhampton Road and rear of the Stan Cullis Stand. Also in City Centre (5 minutes walk)
Coach Parking: By Police direction
Nearest Railway Station: Wolverhampton (¾ mile)
Nearest Bus Station: Wolverhampton (¾ mile)
Club Shop: At the ground
Opening Times: Daily from 9.00am to 5.00pm
Telephone N°: 0371 222-2220 Option 1

GROUND INFORMATION

Away Supporters' Entrances & Sections:
Steve Bull Stand Lower Tier (turnstiles for Block 3)

ADMISSION INFO (2019/2020 PRICES)

Adult Seating: £25.00 – £46.00
Senior Citizen/Under-21s Seating: £15.00 – £26.50
Under-17s Seating: £11.50 – £18.50
Under-12s Seating: £6.00 – £15.00
Programme Price: £3.00

FANS WITH DISABILITIES INFORMATION

Wheelchairs: 115 spaces in total in special sections in the Stan Cullis Stand and Billy Wright Family Enclosure
Helpers: Admitted
Prices: Please contact the club for details
Disabled Toilets: At both ends of the Stan Cullis Stand
Contact: 0371 222-2220 customerservice@wolves.co.uk

Travelling Supporters' Information:
Routes: From North: Exit M6 Junction 12. At island take 3rd exit onto A5 for Wolverhampton. At next island turn left onto A449. After 6 miles A449 passes under M54, carry straight on and at 6th roundabout (Five Ways) take 3rd exit into Waterloo Road. Molineux is 1 mile straight on; From South West: Exit M5 Junction 2, follow signs for Wolverhampton on A4123 for 8 miles to ring road. Turn left on ring road (follow Molineux Centre signs). Take 2nd exit at next 2 islands * Pass Bank's Brewery and Swimming Baths on left and turn left at next set of traffic lights. Molineux is 500 yards on right; From South/East: Exit M6 Junction 10, take A454 (via Willenhall) to Wolverhampton ring road. At first ring road island take 4th exit (A449 to Stafford). Straight on at next 2 sets of traffic lights. Filter right at third set of lights (Waterloo Road). Molineux is 500 yards on right; From West: Take A41 to Wolverhampton ring road roundabout. Turn left into the ring road. Then as from the South West *

WYCOMBE WANDERERS FC

Founded: 1887 (**Entered League**: 1993)
Nickname: 'The Blues' 'The Chairboys'
Ground: Adams Park, Hillbottom Road, Sands, High Wycombe HP12 4HJ
Ground Capacity: 9,448
Seating Capacity: 8,250
Record Attendance: 10,000 (vs Chelsea, July 2005)

Pitch Size: 115 × 75 yards
Colours: Navy and Light Blue quarters with Navy shorts
Telephone Nº: (01494) 472100
Ticket Office: (01494) 441118
Fax Number: (01494) 441589
Web Site: www.wycombewanderers.co.uk
E-mail: wwfc@wwfc.com

GENERAL INFORMATION

Car Parking: Car park at the ground (£5.00)
Coach Parking: Car park at the ground
Nearest Railway Station: High Wycombe
Nearest Bus Station: High Wycombe
Club Shop: At the ground
Opening Times: Monday to Friday 10.00am to 5.00pm but closed on Wednesdays. Also open from 10.00am on Saturday matchdays
Telephone Nº: (01494) 441118

GROUND INFORMATION

Away Supporters' Entrances & Sections:
Dreams Stand (seating only)

ADMISSION INFO (2019/2020 PRICES)

Adult Standing: £18.00 **Adult Seating**: £19.00–£24.00
Ages 19-25 Standing: £14.00 **Seating**: £15.00–£19.00
Ages 13-18 Standing: £8.00 **Seating**: £6.00–£13.00
Senior Citizen Standing: £16.00 **Seating**: £17–£21
Under-12s Standing/Seating: Free of charge
Note: A £2.00 discount is available for advance purchases
Programme Price: £3.50

FANS WITH DISABILITIES INFORMATION

Wheelchairs: 32 spaces in total available in special sections of the Family Stand and Away Stand
Helpers: One helper admitted per wheelchair
Prices: Full price for fans with disabilities. Free for helpers
Disabled Toilets: 4 available in the Family Stand
Commentaries are available for 5 people
Contact: (01494) 441118 (Bookings are not necessary) or e-mail tickets@wwfc.com (Lily Fulker)

Travelling Supporters' Information:
Routes: From All Parts: Exit the M40 at Junction 4 and take the A4010 following Aylesbury signs. Go straight on at 3 mini-roundabouts then bear sharp left at the 4th roundabout into Lane End Road. Fork right into Hillbottom Road at the next roundabout. The ground is at the end of the road. Hillbottom Road is on the Sands Industrial Estate; From the Town Centre: Take the A40 West and after 1½ miles turn left into Chapel Lane (after the traffic lights). Turn right then right again at the mini-roundabout into Lane End Road – then as above.

F.A. Premier League 2018/2019 Season	Arsenal	Bournemouth	Brighton & Hove Albion	Burnley	Cardiff City	Chelsea	Crystal Palace	Everton	Fulham	Huddersfield Town	Leicester City	Liverpool	Manchester City	Manchester United	Newcastle United	Southampton	Tottenham Hotspur	Watford	West Ham United	Wolverhampton Wanderers
Arsenal		5-1	1-1	3-1	2-1	2-0	2-3	2-0	4-1	1-0	3-1	1-1	0-2	2-0	2-0	2-0	4-2	2-0	3-1	1-1
Bournemouth	1-2		2-0	1-3	2-0	4-0	2-1	2-2	0-1	2-1	4-2	0-4	0-1	1-2	2-2	0-0	1-0	3-3	2-0	1-1
Brighton & Hove Albion	1-1	0-5		1-3	0-2	1-2	3-1	1-0	2-2	1-0	1-1	0-1	1-4	3-2	1-1	0-1	1-2	0-0	1-0	1-0
Burnley	1-3	4-0	1-0		2-0	0-4	1-3	1-5	2-1	1-1	1-2	1-3	0-1	0-2	1-2	1-1	2-1	1-3	2-0	2-0
Cardiff City	2-3	2-0	2-1	1-2		1-2	2-3	0-3	4-2	0-0	0-1	0-2	0-5	1-5	0-0	1-0	0-3	1-5	2-0	2-1
Chelsea	3-2	2-0	3-0	2-2	4-1		3-1	0-0	2-0	5-0	0-1	1-1	2-0	2-2	2-1	0-0	2-0	3-0	2-0	1-1
Crystal Palace	2-2	5-3	1-2	2-0	0-0	0-1		0-0	2-0	2-0	1-0	0-2	1-3	1-3	0-0	0-2	0-1	1-2	1-1	0-1
Everton	1-0	2-0	3-1	2-0	1-0	2-0	2-0		3-0	1-1	0-1	0-0	0-2	4-0	1-1	2-1	2-6	2-2	1-3	1-3
Fulham	1-5	0-3	4-2	4-2	1-0	1-2	0-2	2-0		1-0	1-1	1-2	0-2	0-3	0-4	3-2	1-2	1-1	0-2	1-1
Huddersfield Town	1-2	0-2	1-2	1-2	0-0	0-3	0-1	0-1	1-0		1-4	0-1	0-3	1-1	0-1	1-3	0-2	1-2	1-1	1-0
Leicester City	3-0	2-0	2-1	0-0	0-1	0-0	1-4	1-2	3-1	3-1		1-2	2-1	0-1	0-1	1-2	0-2	2-0	1-1	2-0
Liverpool	5-1	3-0	1-0	4-2	4-1	2-0	4-3	1-0	2-0	5-0	1-1		0-0	3-1	4-0	3-0	2-1	5-0	4-0	2-0
Manchester City	3-1	3-1	2-0	5-0	2-0	6-0	2-3	3-1	3-0	6-1	1-0	2-1		3-1	2-1	6-1	1-0	3-1	1-0	3-0
Manchester United	2-2	4-1	2-1	2-2	0-2	1-1	0-0	2-1	4-1	3-1	2-1	0-0	0-2		3-2	3-2	0-3	2-1	2-1	1-1
Newcastle United	1-2	2-1	0-1	2-0	3-0	1-2	0-1	3-2	0-0	2-0	0-2	2-3	2-1	0-2		3-1	1-2	1-0	0-3	1-2
Southampton	3-2	3-3	2-2	0-0	1-2	0-3	1-1	2-1	2-0	1-1	1-2	1-3	1-3	2-2	0-0		2-1	1-1	1-2	3-1
Tottenham Hotspur	1-1	5-0	1-0	1-0	1-0	3-1	2-0	2-2	3-1	4-0	3-1	1-2	0-1	0-1	1-0	3-1		2-1	0-1	1-3
Watford	0-1	0-4	2-0	0-0	3-2	1-2	2-1	1-0	4-1	3-0	2-1	0-3	1-2	1-2	1-1	1-1	2-1		1-4	1-2
West Ham United	1-0	1-2	2-2	4-2	3-1	0-0	3-2	0-2	3-1	4-3	2-2	1-1	0-4	3-1	2-0	3-0	0-1	0-2		0-1
Wolverhampton Wanderers	3-1	2-0	0-0	1-0	2-0	2-1	0-2	2-2	1-0	0-2	4-3	0-2	1-1	2-1	1-1	2-0	2-3	0-2	3-0	

EFL Championship 2018/2019 Season	Aston Villa	Birmingham City	Blackburn Rovers	Bolton Wanderers	Brentford	Bristol City	Derby County	Hull City	Ipswich Town	Leeds United	Middlesbrough	Millwall	Norwich City	Nottingham Forest	Preston North End	Queens Park Rangers	Reading	Rotherham United	Sheffield United	Sheffield Wednesday	Stoke City	Swansea City	West Bromwich Albion	Wigan Athletic
Aston Villa		4-2	2-1	2-0	2-2	2-1	4-0	2-2	2-1	2-3	3-0	1-0	1-2	5-5	3-3	2-2	1-1	2-0	3-3	1-2	2-2	1-0	0-2	3-2
Birmingham City	0-1		2-2	0-1	0-0	0-1	2-2	3-3	2-2	1-0	1-2	0-2	2-2	2-0	3-0	0-0	2-1	3-1	1-1	3-1	2-0	0-0	1-1	1-1
Blackburn Rovers	1-1	2-2		2-0	1-0	0-1	2-0	3-0	2-0	2-1	0-1	0-0	0-1	2-2	0-1	1-0	2-2	1-1	0-2	4-2	0-1	2-2	2-1	3-0
Bolton Wanderers	0-2	1-0	0-1		0-1*	2-2	1-0	0-1	1-2	0-1	0-2	2-1	0-4	0-3	1-2	1-2	1-1	2-1	0-3	0-2	0-0	0-1	0-2	1-1
Brentford	1-0	1-1	5-2	1-0		0-1	3-3	5-1	2-0	2-0	1-2	2-0	1-1	2-1	3-0	3-0	2-2	5-1	2-3	2-0	3-1	2-3	0-1	2-0
Bristol City	1-1	1-2	4-1	2-1	1-1		0-2	1-0	1-1	0-1	0-2	1-1	2-2	1-1	0-1	2-1	1-1	1-0	1-0	1-2	0-1	2-0	3-2	2-2
Derby County	0-3	3-1	0-0	4-0	3-1	1-1		2-0	2-0	1-4	1-1	0-1	1-1	0-0	2-0	2-0	2-1	6-1	2-1	1-1	0-0	2-1	3-1	2-1
Hull City	1-3	2-0	0-1	6-0	2-0	1-1	1-2		2-0	0-1	1-1	2-1	0-0	0-2	1-1	2-2	3-1	2-2	0-3	3-0	2-0	3-2	1-0	2-1
Ipswich Town	1-1	1-1	2-2	0-0	1-1	2-3	1-1	0-2		3-2	0-2	2-3	1-1	1-1	1-1	0-2	1-2	1-0	1-1	0-1	1-1	0-1	1-2	1-0
Leeds United	1-1	1-2	3-2	2-1	1-1	2-0	2-0	0-2	2-0		0-0	3-2	1-3	1-1	3-0	2-1	1-0	2-0	0-1	1-0	3-1	2-1	4-0	1-2
Middlesbrough	0-3	1-0	1-1	2-0	1-2	0-1	1-1	1-0	2-0	1-1		1-1	0-1	0-2	1-2	2-0	2-1	0-0	3-0	0-1	1-0	0-0	1-0	2-0
Millwall	2-1	0-2	0-2	1-1	1-1	1-2	2-1	2-2	3-0	1-1	2-2		1-3	1-0	1-3	0-0	1-0	0-0	2-3	0-0	0-0	1-2	2-0	2-1
Norwich City	2-1	3-1	2-1	3-2	1-0	3-2	3-4	3-2	3-0	0-3	1-0	4-3		3-3	2-0	4-0	2-2	3-1	2-2	2-2	0-1	1-0	3-4	1-0
Nottingham Forest	1-3	2-2	1-2	1-0	2-1	0-1	1-0	3-0	2-0	4-2	3-0	2-2	1-2		0-1	0-1	1-0	1-0	1-0	2-1	0-0	2-1	1-1	3-1
Preston North End	1-1	1-0	4-1	2-2	4-3	1-1	0-0	1-2	4-0	0-2	1-1	3-2	3-1	0-0		1-0	2-3	1-1	0-1	3-3	2-2	1-1	2-3	4-0
Queens Park Rangers	1-0	3-4	1-2	1-2	3-2	0-3	1-1	2-3	3-0	1-0	2-1	2-0	0-1	0-1	1-4		0-0	1-2	1-2	3-0	0-0	4-0	2-3	1-0
Reading	0-0	0-0	2-1	0-1	2-1	3-2	1-2	3-0	2-2	0-3	0-1	3-1	1-2	2-0	2-1	0-1		1-1	0-2	1-2	2-2	1-4	0-0	3-2
Rotherham United	1-2	1-3	3-2	1-1	2-4	0-0	1-0	2-3	1-0	1-2	1-2	1-0	1-2	2-1	2-1	2-2	1-1		2-2	2-2	2-2	2-1	0-4	1-1
Sheffield United	4-1	0-0	3-0	2-0	2-0	2-3	3-1	1-0	2-0	0-1	1-0	1-1	2-1	2-0	3-2	1-0	4-0	2-0		0-0	1-1	1-2	1-2	4-2
Sheffield Wednesday	1-3	1-1	4-2	1-0	2-0	2-0	1-2	1-1	2-1	1-1	1-2	2-1	0-4	3-0	1-0	1-2	0-0	2-2	0-0		2-2	3-1	2-2	1-0
Stoke City	1-1	0-1	2-3	2-0	1-1	0-2	2-1	2-0	2-0	2-1	0-0	1-0	2-2	2-0	0-2	2-2	0-0	2-2	2-2	0-0		1-0	0-1	0-3
Swansea City	0-1	3-3	3-1	2-0	3-0	0-1	1-1	2-2	2-3	2-2	3-1	1-0	1-4	0-0	1-0	3-0	2-0	4-3	1-0	2-1	3-1		1-2	2-2
West Bromwich Albion	2-2	3-2	1-1	1-2	1-1	4-2	1-4	3-2	1-1	4-1	2-3	2-0	1-1	2-2	4-1	7-1	4-1	2-1	0-1	1-1	2-1	3-0		2-0
Wigan Athletic	3-0	0-3	3-1	5-2	0-0	1-0	0-1	2-1	1-1	1-2	0-0	1-0	1-1	2-2	2-0	2-1	0-0	1-0	0-3	3-2	0-0	0-0	1-0	

The match between Bolton Wanderers and Brentford which was scheduled to be played on 7th May 2019 was cancelled after it became apparent that Bolton could not fulfil the fixture due to financial difficulties. The match was awarded to Brentford with a 1-0 scoreline.

EFL League One 2018/2019 Season	Accrington Stanley	AFC Wimbledon	Barnsley	Blackpool	Bradford City	Bristol Rovers	Burton Albion	Charlton Athletic	Coventry City	Doncaster Rovers	Fleetwood Town	Gillingham	Luton Town	Oxford United	Peterborough United	Plymouth Argyle	Portsmouth	Rochdale	Scunthorpe United	Shrewsbury Town	Southend United	Sunderland	Wallsall	Wycombe Wanderers
Accrington Stanley		2-1	0-2	1-2	3-1	0-0	1-1	1-1	0-1	1-0	0-1	0-2	0-3	4-2	0-4	5-1	1-1	0-1	1-1	2-1	1-1	0-3	2-1	1-2
AFC Wimbledon	1-1		1-4	0-0	0-1	1-1	0-2	1-2	0-0	2-0	0-3	2-4	0-2	2-1	1-0	2-1	1-2	1-1	2-3	1-2	2-1	1-2	1-3	2-1
Barnsley	2-0	0-0		2-1	3-0	1-0	0-0	2-1	2-2	1-1	4-2	2-1	3-2	4-0	2-0	1-1	1-1	2-1	2-0	2-1	1-0	0-0	1-1	2-1
Blackpool	1-1	2-0	0-1		3-2	0-3	3-0	2-1	2-0	1-1	2-1	0-3	0-0	0-1	0-1	2-2	1-2	2-2	1-0	0-0	2-2	0-1	2-0	2-2
Bradford City	3-0	0-0	0-2	1-4		0-0	1-0	0-2	2-4	0-1	0-1	1-1	0-1	2-0	3-1	0-0	0-1	0-2	2-0	4-3	0-4	1-2	4-0	1-2
Bristol Rovers	1-2	2-0	2-1	4-0	3-2		0-0	0-0	3-1	0-4	2-1	1-2	1-2	0-0	2-2	0-0	1-2	0-1	1-2	1-1	0-1	0-2	0-1	0-1
Burton Albion	5-2	3-0	3-1	3-0	1-1	1-0		1-2	1-0	1-0	0-1	2-3	2-1	0-0	1-2	1-1	1-2	1-2	0-0	2-1	1-2	2-1	0-0	3-1
Charlton Athletic	1-0	2-0	2-0	0-0	1-0	3-1	2-1		1-2	2-0	0-0	2-0	3-1	1-1	0-1	2-1	2-1	4-0	4-0	2-1	1-1	1-1	2-1	3-2
Coventry City	1-1	1-1	1-0	0-2	2-0	0-0	1-2	2-1		2-1	2-1	1-1	1-2	0-1	1-1	1-0	0-1	0-1	1-2	1-1	1-0	1-1	3-0	1-0
Doncaster Rovers	1-2	2-1	0-0	2-0	2-1	4-1	2-2	1-1	2-0		0-4	3-3	2-1	2-2	3-1	2-0	0-0	5-0	3-0	0-0	3-0	0-1	3-1	3-0
Fleetwood Town	1-1	0-1	1-3	3-2	2-1	0-0	1-0	1-0	3-0	3-0		1-1	1-2	2-2	1-1	2-0	2-5	2-2	0-1	2-1	2-2	2-1	0-0	1-1
Gillingham	0-0	0-1	1-4	0-1	4-0	0-1	3-1	0-2	1-1	1-3	3-0		1-3	1-0	2-4	3-1	2-0	1-1	1-0	0-2	0-2	1-4	0-3	2-2
Luton Town	4-1	2-2	0-0	2-2	4-0	1-0	2-0	2-2	1-1	4-0	2-0	2-2		3-1	4-0	5-1	3-2	2-0	3-2	3-2	2-0	1-1	2-0	3-0
Oxford United	2-3	0-0	2-2	2-0	1-0	0-2	3-1	2-1	1-2	2-2	0-2	1-0	1-2		0-1	2-0	2-1	4-2	2-1	3-0	0-1	1-1	1-2	2-1
Peterborough United	0-1	1-0	0-4	2-2	1-1	2-1	3-1	0-0	1-2	1-1	1-0	2-0	3-1	2-2		0-1	1-2	2-1	0-2	1-2	2-0	1-1	1-1	4-2
Plymouth Argyle	0-3	1-0	0-3	0-1	3-3	2-2	2-3	0-2	2-1	2-3	2-1	3-1	0-0	3-0	1-5		1-1	5-1	3-2	2-1	1-1	0-2	2-1	1-1
Portsmouth	1-1	2-1	0-0	0-1	5-1	1-1	2-2	1-2	2-1	1-1	1-0	0-2	1-0	4-1	2-3	3-0		4-1	2-0	1-1	2-0	3-1	2-0	2-2
Rochdale	1-0	3-4	0-4	2-1	0-4	0-0	0-4	1-0	0-1	2-3	1-1	3-0	0-0	0-0	1-4	1-2	1-3		3-1	2-1	1-0	1-2	1-2	1-0
Scunthorpe United	2-0	1-2	2-2	0-0	2-3	0-1	0-3	5-3	2-1	1-1	0-5	0-2	0-2	3-3	0-2	1-4	1-2	3-3		1-0	4-1	1-1	1-1	1-0
Shrewsbury Town	1-0	0-0	3-1	0-0	0-1	1-1	1-1	0-3	1-0	2-0	0-0	2-2	0-3	2-3	2-2	2-0	0-2	3-2	1-1		2-0	0-2	0-0	2-1
Southend United	3-0	0-1	0-3	1-2	2-0	1-2	3-2	1-2	1-2	2-3	1-0	2-0	0-1	0-0	2-3	2-3	3-3	1-2	2-0	0-2		2-1	3-0	0-2
Sunderland	2-2	1-0	4-2	1-1	1-0	2-1	1-1	2-1	4-5	2-0	1-1	4-2	1-1	1-1	2-2	2-0	1-1	4-1	3-0	1-1	3-0		2-1	1-1
Walsall	0-1	0-1	0-1	0-0	3-2	1-3	1-3	0-2	2-1	1-4	2-0	2-1	2-2	1-3	3-0	2-1	2-3	1-2	1-2	0-0	1-1	2-2		3-2
Wycombe Wanderers	1-3	1-2	1-0	0-0	0-0	1-2	2-1	0-1	0-2	3-2	1-0	0-1	1-1	0-0	1-0	1-0	2-3	3-0	3-2	3-2	2-3	1-1	1-0	

EFL League Two 2018/2019 Season	Bury	Cambridge United	Carlisle United	Cheltenham Town	Colchester United	Crawley Town	Crewe Alexandra	Exeter City	Forest Green Rovers	Grimsby Town	Lincoln City	Macclesfield Town	Mansfield Town	Milton Keynes Dons	Morecambe	Newport County	Northampton Town	Notts County	Oldham Athletic	Port Vale	Stevenage	Swindon Town	Tranmere Rovers	Yeovil Town
Bury		0-3	0-1	4-1	2-0	1-1	3-1	2-0	1-1	4-0	3-3	3-0	2-2	4-3	3-2	1-1	3-1	4-0	3-1	1-1	4-0	1-3	2-1	1-0
Cambridge United	2-2		1-2	0-1	0-1	2-1	0-0	0-2	1-3	1-0	1-2	1-0	1-1	0-1	1-2	0-3	3-2	3-2	1-1	1-0	2-0	0-0	0-0	0-0
Carlisle United	3-2	2-2		2-0	4-0	4-2	1-0	1-1	1-2	0-1	1-0	2-1	3-2	2-3	0-2	3-2	2-2	1-3	6-0	2-1	0-1	2-1	0-2	0-1
Cheltenham Town	1-1	2-0	0-1		1-3	0-1	0-0	1-1	2-2	2-1	0-2	3-2	2-2	3-1	2-2	2-1	3-1	4-1	0-0	1-0	0-2	3-2	1-3	1-0
Colchester United	1-2	3-0	1-1	3-0		3-1	6-0	1-1	0-3	1-0	1-0	1-0	2-3	2-0	0-0	3-0	1-2	3-3	0-2	2-0	1-2	1-0	0-2	3-1
Crawley Town	3-2	2-0	2-3	1-0	2-0		3-0	1-1	1-2	2-1	0-3	1-1	0-0	0-4	2-0	4-1	0-1	1-1	0-3	0-1	1-3	2-2	3-1	3-1
Crewe Alexandra	1-1	2-0	2-1	1-3	2-1	6-1		1-2	4-3	2-0	2-1	3-0	0-3	0-0	6-0	3-2	0-2	3-0	0-2	0-1	1-0	1-0	3-2	2-0
Exeter City	0-1	1-0	3-1	3-1	3-0	1-3	1-0		1-2	1-2	0-3	0-1	1-4	3-1	0-0	1-1	2-2	5-1	1-0	2-0	1-0	2-0	0-1	2-1
Forest Green Rovers	1-2	2-1	1-1	1-1	0-1	1-0	1-0	0-0		3-0	1-2	2-0	1-1	1-2	0-1	1-1	2-1	1-2	1-1	1-1	0-0	1-1	3-1	3-0
Grimsby Town	0-0	0-2	1-0	1-0	1-0	1-0	2-0	0-0	1-4		1-1	0-2	0-1	1-0	1-2	3-0	0-0	4-0	0-3	2-0	0-2	2-1	5-2	0-1
Lincoln City	2-1	1-1	2-2	1-1	0-3	0-1	1-0	1-1	2-1	1-0		1-1	1-1	2-1	3-1	3-2	1-1	3-1	2-0	1-1	2-2	4-1	0-0	1-0
Macclesfield Town	1-4	1-1	2-1	1-1	1-1	2-0	3-3	3-2	1-1	0-2	1-2		1-1	1-3	1-1	0-0	0-5	0-1	2-1	0-0	2-2	1-2	1-1	1-0
Mansfield Town	2-1	1-0	1-0	4-2	1-1	1-0	1-2	1-2	1-0	2-1	1-1	3-1		1-1	4-0	3-0	4-0	2-0	0-0	1-0	1-2	0-0	3-0	0-1
Milton Keynes Dons	1-0	6-0	2-0	3-0	0-1	1-0	0-1	1-0	1-1	1-1	0-2	2-0	1-0		2-0	2-0	1-0	2-1	2-1	1-1	1-1	2-3	1-1	2-0
Morecambe	2-3	3-0	0-2	4-0	0-1	1-0	2-2	0-2	3-0	1-1	0-2	2-1	0-1	4-2		1-1	1-0	1-1	0-2	2-2	1-2	0-1	3-4	2-1
Newport County	3-1	4-2	2-0	1-0	2-0	0-0	1-0	1-0	1-4	1-0	1-0	3-3	1-0	0-1	1-1		3-1	3-2	2-0	0-0	2-1	0-0	0-0	0-6
Northampton Town	0-0	2-2	3-0	1-3	0-4	0-0	2-0	2-1	2-1	2-2	0-1	3-1	1-1	2-2	1-1	1-0		0-0	2-1	1-2	1-1	1-1	1-1	2-2
Notts County	0-0	0-1	1-1	0-3	0-0	3-1	2-1	0-1	1-3	2-1	1-1	1-2	1-0	1-2	0-0	1-4	2-2		0-0	0-0	3-3	1-2	3-2	0-4
Oldham Athletic	4-2	3-1	1-3	2-0	3-3	2-1	1-1	2-3	0-0	2-0	1-1	3-1	3-2	1-2	1-2	0-1	2-5	2-0		0-1	1-1	2-2	2-0	4-1
Port Vale	1-0	3-0	0-1	2-2	0-3	1-0	1-0	1-1	0-2	0-1	2-6	0-1	2-1	0-2	0-1	1-2	2-0	2-2	1-4		1-4	0-1	1-2	3-0
Stevenage	0-1	0-1	3-0	2-0	3-1	2-1	0-1	1-1	0-2	1-0	0-1	1-0	1-3	3-2	1-0	1-0	1-2	0-3	3-2	0-0		2-0	2-2	1-0
Swindon Town	1-2	0-2	0-4	0-0	3-0	0-1	1-2	0-2	2-0	1-1	2-2	3-2	0-0	1-1	4-0	2-1	1-1	3-1	0-0	0-0	3-2		3-2	1-1
Tranmere Rovers	1-1	1-0	3-0	1-0	1-1	5-1	1-0	2-0	0-1	4-1	1-0	1-0	0-0	2-1	3-1	0-1	1-2	1-0	1-1	1-0	2-0	1-2		0-0
Yeovil Town	0-1	1-0	0-0	1-4	1-1	0-1	1-1	2-2	1-2	1-3	0-2	0-2	2-2	1-1	3-2	1-3	1-1	2-0	0-0	0-3	2-0	0-3	0-0	

F.A. Premier League

Season 2018/2019

Manchester City	38	32	2	4	95	23	98
Liverpool	38	30	7	1	89	22	97
Chelsea	38	21	9	8	63	39	72
Tottenham Hotspur	38	23	2	13	67	39	71
Arsenal	38	21	7	10	73	51	70
Manchester United	38	19	9	10	65	54	66
Wolverhampton Wanderers	38	16	9	13	47	46	57
Everton	38	15	9	14	54	46	54
Leicester City	38	15	7	16	51	48	52
West Ham United	38	15	7	16	52	55	52
Watford	38	14	8	16	52	59	50
Crystal Palace	38	14	7	17	51	53	49
Newcastle United	38	12	9	17	42	48	45
Bournemouth	38	13	6	19	56	70	45
Burnley	38	11	7	20	45	68	40
Southampton	38	9	12	17	45	65	39
Brighton & Hove Albion	38	9	9	20	35	60	36
Cardiff City	38	10	4	24	34	69	34
Fulham	38	7	5	26	34	81	26
Huddersfield Town	38	3	7	28	22	76	16

Champions: Manchester City

Relegated: Cardiff City, Fulham and Huddersfield Town

EFL Championship

Season 2018/2019

Norwich City	46	27	13	6	93	57	94
Sheffield United	46	26	11	9	78	41	89
Leeds United	46	25	8	13	73	50	83
West Bromwich Albion	46	23	11	12	87	62	80
Aston Villa	46	20	16	10	82	61	76
Derby County	46	20	14	12	69	54	74
Middlesbrough	46	20	13	13	49	41	73
Bristol City	46	19	13	14	59	53	70
Nottingham Forest	46	17	15	14	61	54	66
Swansea City	46	18	11	17	65	62	65
Brentford	46	17	13	16	73	59	64
Sheffield Wednesday	46	16	16	14	60	62	64
Hull City	46	17	11	18	66	68	62
Preston North End	46	16	13	17	67	67	61
Blackburn Rovers	46	16	12	18	64	69	60
Stoke City	46	11	22	13	45	52	55
Birmingham City	46	14	19	13	64	58	52
Wigan Athletic	46	13	13	20	51	64	52
Queens Park Rangers	46	14	9	23	53	71	51
Reading	46	10	17	19	49	66	47
Millwall	46	10	14	22	48	64	44
Rotherham United	46	8	16	22	52	83	40
Bolton Wanderers	46	8	8	30	29	78	32
Ipswich Town	46	5	16	25	36	77	31

Bolton Wanderers vs Brentford was cancelled after Bolton could not fulfil the fixture due to financial difficulties. The match was awarded to Brentford with a 1-0 scoreline.

Birmingham City had 9 points deducted for failure to comply with the EFL profitability and Sustainability rules

Promotion Play-offs

Aston Villa .... 2 West Bromwich Albion 1
Derby County .... 0 Leeds United 1

West Bromwich Albion .... 1 Aston Villa 0
Aggregate 2-2. Aston Villa won 4-3 on penalties
Leeds United .... 2 Derby County 4
Derby County won 4-3 on aggregate.

Aston Villa .... 2 Derby County 1

Promoted: Norwich City, Sheffield United and Aston Villa

Relegated: Rotherham United, Bolton Wanderers and Ipswich Town

EFL League One

Season 2018/2019

Team							
Luton Town	46	27	13	6	90	42	94
Barnsley	46	26	13	7	80	39	91
Charlton Athletic	46	26	10	10	73	40	88
Portsmouth	46	25	13	8	83	51	88
Sunderland	46	22	19	5	80	47	85
Doncaster Rovers	46	20	13	13	76	58	73
Peterborough United	46	20	12	14	71	62	72
Coventry City	46	18	11	17	54	54	65
Burton Albion	46	17	12	17	66	57	63
Blackpool	46	15	17	14	50	52	62
Fleetwood Town	46	16	13	17	58	52	61
Oxford United	46	15	15	16	58	64	60
Gillingham	46	15	10	21	61	72	55
Accrington Stanley	46	14	13	19	51	67	55
Bristol Rovers	46	13	15	18	47	50	54
Rochdale	46	15	9	22	54	87	54
Wycombe Wanderers	46	14	11	21	55	67	53
Shrewsbury Town	46	12	16	18	51	59	52
Southend United	46	14	8	24	55	68	50
AFC Wimbledon	46	13	11	22	42	63	50
Plymouth Argyle	46	13	11	22	56	80	50
Walsall	46	12	11	23	49	71	47
Scunthorpe United	46	12	10	24	53	83	46
Bradford City	46	11	8	27	49	77	41

Promotion Play-offs

Sunderland .... 1 Portsmouth 0
Doncaster Rovers .... 1 Charlton Athletic 2

Portsmouth .... 0 Sunderland 0
Sunderland won 1-0 on aggregate.
Charlton Athletic .... 2 Doncaster Rovers .... 3 (aet)
Aggregate 3-3. Charlton Athletic won 4-3 on penalties

Charlton Athletic .... 2 Sunderland 1

Promoted: Luton Town, Barnsley and Charlton Athletic

Relegated: Plymouth Argyle, Walsall, Scunthorpe United and Bradford City

EFL League Two

Season 2018/2019

Team							
Lincoln City	46	23	16	7	73	43	85
Bury	46	22	13	11	82	56	79
Milton Keynes Dons	46	23	10	13	71	49	79
Mansfield Town	46	20	16	10	69	41	76
Forest Green Rovers	46	20	14	12	68	47	74
Tranmere Rovers	46	20	13	13	63	50	73
Newport County	46	20	11	15	59	59	71
Colchester United	46	20	10	16	65	53	70
Exeter City	46	19	13	14	60	49	70
Stevenage	46	20	10	16	59	55	70
Carlisle United	46	20	8	18	67	62	68
Crewe Alexandra	46	19	8	19	60	59	65
Swindon Town	46	16	16	14	59	56	64
Oldham Athletic	46	16	14	16	67	60	62
Northampton Town	46	14	19	13	64	63	61
Cheltenham Town	46	15	12	19	57	68	57
Grimsby Town	46	16	8	22	45	56	56
Morecambe	46	14	12	20	54	70	54
Crawley Town	46	15	8	23	51	68	53
Port Vale	46	12	13	21	39	55	49
Cambridge United	46	12	11	23	40	66	47
Macclesfield Town	46	10	14	22	48	74	44
Notts County	46	9	14	23	48	84	41
Yeovil Town	46	9	13	24	41	66	40

Promotion Play-offs

Newport County .... 1 Mansfield Town 1
Tranmere Rovers .... 1 Forest Green Rovers 0

Mansfield Town .... 0 Newport County .... 0 (aet)
Aggregate 1-1. Newport County won 5-3 on penalties.
Forest Green Rovers .... 1 Tranmere Rovers 1
Tranmere Rovers won 2-1 on aggregate.

Newport County .... 0 Tranmere Rovers 1

Promoted: Lincoln City, Bury, Milton Keynes Dons and Tranmere Rovers

Relegated: Notts County and Yeovil Town

F.A. Cup 2018/2019

Round 1	Accrington Stanley	1	Colchester United	0	
Round 1	Aldershot Town	1	Bradford City	1	
Round 1	Alfreton Town	1	Fleetwood Town	4	
Round 1	Barnet	1	Bristol Rovers	1	
Round 1	Barnsley	4	Notts County	0	
Round 1	Bromley	1	Peterborough United	3	
Round 1	Bury	5	Dover Athletic	0	
Round 1	Chesterfield	1	Billericay Town	1	
Round 1	Chorley	2	Doncaster Rovers	2	
Round 1	Crewe Alexandra	0	Carlisle United	1	
Round 1	Ebbsfleet United	0	Cheltenham Town	0	
Round 1	Exeter City	2	Blackpool	3	
Round 1	Gillingham	0	Hartlepool United	0	
Round 1	Grimsby Town	3	Milton Keynes Dons	1	
Round 1	Guiseley	4	Cambridge United	3	
Round 1	Hampton & Richmond Borough	1	Oldham Athletic	2	
Round 1	Haringey Borough	0	AFC Wimbledon	1	
Round 1	Hitchin Town	0	Solihull Moors	2	
Round 1	Lincoln City	3	Northampton Town	2	
Round 1	Luton Town	2	Wycombe Wanderers	0	
Round 1	Maidenhead United	0	Portsmouth	4	
Round 1	Maidstone United	2	Macclesfield Town	1	
Round 1	Mansfield Town	1	Charlton Athletic	1	
Round 1	Metropolitan Police	0	Newport County	2	
Round 1	Morecambe	0	FC Halifax Town	0	
Round 1	Oxford United	0	Forest Green Rovers	0	
Round 1	Plymouth Argyle	1	Stevenage	0	
Round 1	Port Vale	1	Sunderland	2	
Round 1	Rochdale	2	Gateshead	1	
Round 1	Scunthorpe United	2	Burton Albion	1	
Round 1	Shrewsbury Town	1	Salford City	1	
Round 1	Southend United	1	Crawley Town	1	
Round 1	Southport	2	Boreham Wood	0	
Round 1	Sutton United	0	Slough Town	0	
Round 1	Swindon Town	2	York City	1	
Round 1	Torquay United	0	Woking	1	
Round 1	Tranmere Rovers	3	Oxford City	3	
Round 1	Walsall	3	Coventry City	2	
Round 1	Weston-Super-Mare	0	Wrexham	2	
Round 1	Yeovil Town	1	Stockport County	3	
Replay	Billericay Town	1	Chesterfield	3	
Replay	Bradford City	1	Aldershot Town	1	(aet)
	Bradford City won 4-1 on penalties.				
Replay	Bristol Rovers	1	Barnet	2	
Replay	Charlton Athletic	5	Mansfield Town	0	
Replay	Cheltenham Town	2	Ebbsfleet United	0	
Replay	Crawley Town	2	Southend United	6	(aet)
Replay	Doncaster Rovers	7	Chorley	0	
Replay	FC Halifax Town	1	Morecambe	0	
Replay	Forest Green Rovers	0	Oxford United	3	
Replay	Hartlepool United	3	Gillingham	4 (aet)	
Replay	Oxford City	0	Tranmere Rovers	2	
Replay	Salford City	1	Shrewsbury Town	3	

Replay	Slough Town	1	Sutton United	1	(aet)
	Slough Town won 8-7 on penalties.				
Round 2	Accrington Stanley	3	Cheltenham Town	1	
Round 2	Barnet	1	Stockport County	0	
Round 2	Bury	0	Luton Town	1	
Round 2	Charlton Athletic	0	Doncaster Rovers	2	
Round 2	Chesterfield	0	Grimsby Town	2	
Round 2	FC Halifax Town	1	AFC Wimbledon	3	
Round 2	Guiseley	1	Fleetwood Town	2	
Round 2	Lincoln City	2	Carlisle United	0	
Round 2	Maidstone United	0	Oldham Athletic	2	
Round 2	Peterborough United	2	Bradford City	2	
Round 2	Plymouth Argyle	1	Oxford United	2	
Round 2	Rochdale	0	Portsmouth	1	
Round 2	Shrewsbury Town	1	Scunthorpe United	0	
Round 2	Slough Town	0	Gillingham	1	
Round 2	Solihull Moors	0	Blackpool	0	
Round 2	Southend United	2	Barnsley	4	
Round 2	Swindon Town	0	Woking	1	
Round 2	Tranmere Rovers	1	Southport	1	
Round 2	Walsall	1	Sunderland	1	
Round 2	Wrexham	0	Newport County	0	
Replay	Blackpool	3	Solihull Moors	2	(aet)
Replay	Bradford City	4	Peterborough United	4	(aet)
	Peterborough United won 3-2 on penalties.				
Replay	Newport County	4	Wrexham	0	
Replay	Southport	0	Tranmere Rovers	2	
Replay	Sunderland	0	Walsall	1	
Round 3	Accrington Stanley	1	Ipswich Town	0	
Round 3	Aston Villa	0	Swansea City	3	
Round 3	Blackpool	0	Arsenal	3	
Round 3	Bolton Wanderers	5	Walsall	2	
Round 3	AFC Bournemouth	1	Brighton & Hove Albion	3	
Round 3	Brentford	1	Oxford United	0	
Round 3	Bristol City	1	Huddersfield Town	0	
Round 3	Burnley	1	Barnsley	0	
Round 3	Chelsea	2	Nottingham Forest	0	
Round 3	Crystal Palace	1	Grimsby Town	0	
Round 3	Derby County	2	Southampton	2	
Round 3	Everton	2	Lincoln City	1	
Round 3	Fleetwood Town	2	AFC Wimbledon	3	
Round 3	Fulham	1	Oldham Athletic	2	
Round 3	Gillingham	1	Cardiff City	0	
Round 3	Manchester City	7	Rotherham United	0	
Round 3	Manchester United	2	Reading	0	
Round 3	Middlesbrough	5	Peterborough United	0	
Round 3	Millwall	2	Hull City	1	
Round 3	Newcastle United	1	Blackburn Rovers	1	
Round 3	Newport County	2	Leicester City	1	
Round 3	Norwich City	0	Portsmouth	1	
Round 3	Preston North End	1	Doncaster Rovers	3	
Round 3	Queen's Park Rangers	2	Leeds United	1	
Round 3	Sheffield United	0	Barnet	1	
Round 3	Sheffield Wednesday	0	Luton Town	0	

Round 3	Shrewsbury Town	1	Stoke City	1	
Round 3	Tranmere Rovers	0	Tottenham Hotspur	7	
Round 3	West Bromwich Albion	1	Wigan Athletic	0	
Round 3	West Ham United	2	Birmingham City	0	
Round 3	Woking	0	Watford	2	
Round 3	Wolverhampton Wanderers	2	Liverpool	1	
Replay	Blackburn Rovers	2	Newcastle United	4	(aet)
Replay	Luton Town	0	Sheffield Wednesday	1	
Replay	Southampton	2	Derby County	2	(aet)
	Derby County won 5-3 on penalties.				
Replay	Stoke City	2	Shrewsbury Town	3	
Round 4	AFC Wimbledon	4	West Ham United	2	
Round 4	Accrington Stanley	0	Derby County	1	
Round 4	Arsenal	1	Manchester United	3	
Round 4	Barnet	3	Brentford	3	
Round 4	Brighton & Hove Albion	0	West Bromwich Albion	0	
Round 4	Bristol City	2	Bolton Wanderers	1	
Round 4	Chelsea	3	Sheffield Wednesday	0	
Round 4	Crystal Palace	2	Tottenham Hotspur	0	
Round 4	Doncaster Rovers	2	Oldham Athletic	1	
Round 4	Manchester City	5	Burnley	0	
Round 4	Middlesbrough	1	Newport County	1	
Round 4	Millwall	3	Everton	2	
Round 4	Newcastle United	0	Watford	2	
Round 4	Portsmouth	1	Queen's Park Rangers	1	
Round 4	Shrewsbury Town	2	Wolverhampton Wanderers	2	
Round 4	Swansea City	4	Gillingham	1	
Replay	Brentford	3	Barnet	1	
Replay	Newport County	2	Middlesbrough	0	
Replay	Queen's Park Rangers	2	Portsmouth	0	
Replay	West Bromwich Albion	1	Brighton & Hove Albion	3	(aet)
Replay	Wolverhampton Wanderers	3	Shrewsbury Town	2	
Round 5	AFC Wimbledon	0	Millwall	1	
Round 5	Brighton & Hove Albion	2	Derby County	1	
Round 5	Bristol City	0	Wolverhampton Wanderers	1	
Round 5	Chelsea	0	Manchester United	2	
Round 5	Doncaster Rovers	0	Crystal Palace	2	
Round 5	Newport County	1	Manchester City	4	
Round 5	Queen's Park Rangers	0	Watford	1	
Round 5	Swansea City	4	Brentford	1	
Round 6	Millwall	2	Brighton & Hove Albion	2	(aet)
	Brighton & Hove Albion won 5-4 on penalties.				
Round 6	Swansea City	2	Manchester City	3	
Round 6	Watford	2	Crystal Palace	1	
Round 6	Wolverhampton Wanderers	2	Manchester United	1	
Semi-final	Manchester City	1	Brighton & Hove Albion	0	
Semi-final	Watford	3	Wolverhampton Wanderers	2	(aet)
FINAL	Manchester City	6	Watford	0	

Cup Statistics courtesy of www.soccerdata.com

English Football League Cup 2018/2019

Round	Home		Away	
Round 1	Blackpool	3	Barnsley	1
Round 1	Bristol City	0	Plymouth Argyle	1
Round 1	Bristol Rovers	2	Crawley Town	1
Round 1	Cambridge United	1	Newport County	4
Round 1	Carlisle United	1	Blackburn Rovers	5
Round 1	Cheltenham Town	2	Colchester United	2
	Cheltenham Town won 6-5 on penalties			
Round 1	Crewe Alexandra	1	Fleetwood Town	1
	Fleetwood Town won 4-3 on penalties.			
Round 1	Exeter City	1	Ipswich Town	1
	Exeter City won 4-2 on penalties			
Round 1	Grimsby Town	0	Rochdale	2
Round 1	Leeds United	2	Bolton Wanderers	1
Round 1	Macclesfield Town	1	Bradford City	1
	Macclesfield Town won 4-2 on penalties.			
Round 1	Mansfield Town	6	Accrington Stanley	1
Round 1	Middlesbrough	3	Notts County	3
	Middlesbrough won 4-3 on penalties.			
Round 1	Millwall	0	Gillingham	0
	Millwall won 3-1 on penalties.			
Round 1	Milton Keynes Dons	3	Charlton Athletic	0
Round 1	Norwich City	3	Stevenage	1
Round 1	Nottingham Forest	1	Bury	1
	Nottingham Forest won 10-9 on penalties.			
Round 1	Oldham Athletic	0	Derby County	2
Round 1	Oxford United	2	Coventry City	0
Round 1	Port Vale	0	Lincoln City	4
Round 1	Portsmouth	1	AFC Wimbledon	2
Round 1	Preston North End	3	Morecambe	1
Round 1	Queen's Park Rangers	2	Peterborough United	0
Round 1	Reading	2	Birmingham City	0
Round 1	Rotherham United	3	Wigan Athletic	1
Round 1	Scunthorpe United	1	Doncaster Rovers	2
Round 1	Sheffield United	1	Hull City	1
	Hull City won 5-4 on penalties.			
Round 1	Shrewsbury Town	1	Burton Albion	2
Round 1	Southend United	2	Brentford	4
Round 1	Sunderland	0	Sheffield Wednesday	2
Round 1	Swindon Town	0	Forest Green Rovers	1
Round 1	Tranmere Rovers	1	Walsall	3
Round 1	West Bromwich Albion	1	Luton Town	0
Round 1	Wycombe Wanderers	1	Northampton Town	1
	Wycombe Wanderers won 7-6 on penalties.			
Round 1	Yeovil Town	0	Aston Villa	1
Round 2	AFC Bournemouth	3	Milton Keynes Dons	0
Round 2	AFC Wimbledon	1	West Ham United	3
Round 2	Blackburn Rovers	4	Lincoln City	1
Round 2	Brentford	1	Cheltenham Town	0
Round 2	Brighton & Hove Albion	0	Southampton	1
Round 2	Burton Albion	1	Aston Villa	0
Round 2	Cardiff City	1	Norwich City	3
Round 2	Doncaster Rovers	1	Blackpool	2
Round 2	Everton	3	Rotherham United	1

Round 2	Fulham	2	Exeter City	0
Round 2	Hull City	0	Derby County	4
Round 2	Leeds United	0	Preston North End	2
Round 2	Leicester City	4	Fleetwood Town	0
Round 2	Middlesbrough	2	Rochdale	1
Round 2	Millwall	3	Plymouth Argyle	2
Round 2	Newport County	0	Oxford United	3
Round 2	Nottingham Forest	3	Newcastle United	1
Round 2	Queen's Park Rangers	3	Bristol Rovers	1
Round 2	Reading	0	Watford	2
Round 2	Sheffield Wednesday	0	Wolverhampton Wanderers	2
Round 2	Stoke City	2	Huddersfield Town	0
Round 2	Swansea City	0	Crystal Palace	1
Round 2	Walsall	3	Macclesfield Town	3
	Macclesfield Town won 3-1 on penalties.			
Round 2	West Bromwich Albion	2	Mansfield Town	1
Round 2	Wycombe Wanderers	2	Forest Green Rovers	2
	Wycombe Wanderers won 4-3 on penalties.			
Round 3	Blackpool	2	Queen's Park Rangers	0
Round 3	AFC Bournemouth	3	Blackburn Rovers	2
Round 3	Burton Albion	2	Burnley	1
Round 3	Millwall	1	Fulham	3
Round 3	Oxford United	0	Manchester City	3
Round 3	Preston North End	2	Middlesbrough	2
	Middlesbrough won 4-3 on penalties.			
Round 3	Wolverhampton Wanderers	0	Leicester City	0
	Leicester City won 3-1 on penalties.			
Round 3	Wycombe Wanderers	3	Norwich City	4
Round 3	Manchester United	2	Derby County	2
	Derby County won 8-7 on penalties.			
Round 3	West Bromwich Albion	0	Crystal Palace	3
Round 3	Arsenal	3	Brentford	1
Round 3	Liverpool	1	Chelsea	2
Round 3	Nottingham Forest	3	Stoke City	2
Round 3	West Ham United	8	Macclesfield Town	0
Round 3	Tottenham Hotspur	2	Watford	2
	Tottenham Hotspur won 4-2 on penalties.			
Round 3	Everton	1	Southampton	1
	Southampton won 4-3 on penalties.			
Round 4	AFC Bournemouth	2	Norwich City	1
Round 4	Burton Albion	3	Nottingham Forest	2
Round 4	Arsenal	2	Blackpool	1
Round 4	Chelsea	3	Derby County	2
Round 4	West Ham United	1	Tottenham Hotspur	3
Round 4	Middlesbrough	1	Crystal Palace	0
Round 4	Manchester City	2	Fulham	0
Round 4	Leicester City	0	Southampton	0
	Leicester City won 6-5 on penalties.			
Round 5	Leicester City	1	Manchester City	1
	Manchester City won 3-1 on penalties.			
Round 5	Middlesbrough	0	Burton Albion	1
Round 5	Arsenal	0	Tottenham Hotspur	2
Round 5	Chelsea	1	AFC Bourenmouth	0

Semi-finals					
1st leg	Tottenham Hotspur	1	Chelsea	0	
1st leg	Manchester City	9	Burton Albion	0	
2nd leg	Chelsea	2	Tottenham Hotspur	1	
	Aggregate 2-2. Chelsea won 4-2 on penalties.				
2nd leg	Burton Albion	0	Manchester City	1	
	Manchester City won 10-0 on aggregate.				
FINAL	Manchester City	0	Chelsea	0	(aet)
	Manchester City won 4-3 on penalties				

Cup Statistics courtesy of www.soccerdata.com

ENGLAND INTERNATIONAL LINE-UPS AND STATISTICS 2018

7th June 2018
v COSTA RICA *Leeds*

J. Butland	Stoke City (sub. N. Pope 65)
P. Jones	Manchester United
J. Stones	Manchester City (sub. G. Cahill 65)
H. Maguire	Leicester City
J. Henderson	Liverpool (sub. D. Alli 64)
T. Alexander-Arnold	Liverpool (sub. K. Trippier 64)
R. Loftus-Cheek	Chelsea (sub. J. Lingard 79)
F. Delph	Manchester City
D. Rose	Tottenham Hotspur
J. Vardy	Leicester City (sub. D. Welbeck 61)
M. Rashford	Manchester City

Result 2-0 Rashford, Welbeck

18th June 2018
v TUNISIA (WC) *Volgograd*

J. Pickford	Everton
K. Walker	Manchester City
J. Stones	Manchester City
H. Maguire	Leicester City
J. Henderson	Liverpool
K. Trippier	Tottenham Hotspur
J. Lingard	Man. United (sub. E. Dier 90+3)
D. Alli	Tottenham Hotspur (sub. R. Loftus-Cheek 80)
A. Young	Manchester United
R. Sterling	Man. City (sub. M. Rashford 68)
H. Kane	Tottenham Hotspur

Result 2-1 Kane

24th June 2018
v PANAMA (WC) *Nizhny Novgorod*

J. Pickford	Everton
K. Walker	Manchester City
J. Stones	Manchester City
H. Maguire	Leicester City
J. Henderson	Liverpool
K. Trippier	Tottenham Hotspur (sub. D. Rose 70)
R. Loftus-Cheek	Chelsea
J. Lingard	Manchester United (sub. F. Delph 63)
A. Young	Manchester United
R. Sterling	Manchester City
H. Kane	Tottenham Hotspur (sub. J. Vardy 63)

Result 6-1 Stones 2, Kane 3 (2 pens), Lingard

28th June 2018
v BELGIUM (WC) *Kaliningrad*

J. Pickford	Everton
P. Jones	Manchester United
J. Stones	Manchester City (sub. H. Maguire 45)
G.Cahill	Chelsea
E. Dier	Tottenham Hotspur
T. Alexander-Arnold	Liverpool (sub. D. Welbeck 79)
R. Loftus-Cheek	Chelsea
F. Delph	Manchester United
D. Rose	Tottenham Hotspur
J. Vardy	Leicester City
M. Rashford	Manchester United

Result 0-1

3rd July 2018
v COLOMBIA (WC) *Moscow*

J. Pickford	Everton
K. Walker	Man. City (sub. M. Rashford 113)
J. Stones	Manchester City
H. Maguire	Leicester City
J. Henderson	Liverpool
K. Trippier	Tottenham Hotspur
J. Lingard	Manchester United
D. Alli	Tottenham Hotspur (sub. E. Dier 81)
A. Young	Man. United (sub. D. Rose 102)
R. Sterling	Manchester City (sub. J. Vardy 88)
H. Kane	Tottenham Hotspur

Result 1-1 Kane (pen)
England won 4-3 on penalties after extra time

7th July 2018
v SWEDEN (WC) *Samara*

J. Pickford	Everton
K. Walker	Manchester City
J. Stones	Manchester City
H. Maguire	Leicester City
J. Henderson	Liverpool (sub. E. Dier 85)
K. Trippier	Tottenham Hotspur
J. Lingard	Manchester United
D. Alli	Tottenham Hotspur (sub. F. Delph 77)
A. Young	Manchester United
R. Sterling	Man. City (sub. M. Rashford 90+1)
H. Kane	Tottenham Hotspur

Result 2-0 Maguire, Alli

ENGLAND INTERNATIONAL LINE-UPS AND STATISTICS 2018

11th July 2018
v CROATIA (WC) *Moscow*

J. Pickford	Everton
K. Walker	Manchester City (sub. J. Vardy 112)
J. Stones	Manchester City
H. Maguire	Leicester City
J. Henderson	Liverpoool (sub. E. Dier 97)
K. Trippier	Tottenham Hotspur
J. Lingard	Manchester United
D. Alli	Tottenham Hotspur
A. Young	Manchester United (sub. D. Rose 90)
H. Kane	Tottenham Hotspur
R. Sterling	Man. City (sub. M. Rashford 74)

Result 1-2 (aet) Trippier

14th July 2018
v BELGIUM (WC) *St. Petersburg*

J. Pickford	Everton
P. Jones	Manchester United
J. Stones	Manchester City
H. Maguire	Leicester City
E. Dier	Tottenham Hotspur
K. Trippier	Tottenham Hotspur
R. Loftus-Cheek	Chelsea (sub. D. Alli 84)
F. Delph	Manchester City
D. Rose	Tottenham H. (sub. J. Lingard 45)
H. Kane	Tottenham Hotspur
R. Sterling	Man. City (sub. M. Rashford 45)

Result 0-2

8th September 2018
v SPAIN (Nations League) *Wembley*

J. Pickford	Everton
J. Gomez	Liverpool
J. Stones	Manchester City
H. Maguire	Leicester City
K. Trippier	Tottenham Hotspur
J. Henderson	Liverpool (sub. E. Dier 64)
D. Alli	Tottenham Hotspur
J. Lingard	Manchester United
L. Shaw	Manchester United (sub. D. Rose 54)
M. Rashford	Man. United (sub. D. Welbeck 90+4)
H. Kane	Tottenham Hotspur

Result 1-2 Rashford

11th September 2019
v SWITZERLAND *Leicester*

J. Butland	Stoke City
K. Walker	Manchester City
J. Tarkowski	Burnley (sub. J. Stones 61)
H. Maguire	Leicester City
E. Dier	Tottenham Hotspur
T. Alexander-Arnold	Liverpool (sub. K. Trippier 78)
R. Loftus-Cheek	Chelsea (sub. J. Lingard 61)
F. Delph	Man. City (sub J. Henderson 68)
D. Rose	Tott. Hotspur (sub. B. Chilwell 79)
M. Rashford	Manchester United
D. Welbeck	Arsenal (sub. H. Kane 61)

Result 1-0 Rashford

12th October 2018
v CROATIA (NL) *Rijeka*

J. Pickford	Everton
K. Walker	Manchester City
J. Stones	Manchester City
H. Maguire	Leicester City
B. Chilwell	Leicester City
E. Dier	Tottenham Hotspur
R. Barkley	Chelsea
J. Henderson	Liverpool
M. Rashford	Manchester United
H. Kane	Tottenham Hotspur
R. Sterling	Manchester City (sub. J. Sancho 78)

Result 0-0

15th October 2018
v SPAIN (NL) *Sevilla*

J. Pickford	Everton
K. Trippier	Tott. Hotspur (sub. T. Alexander-Arnold 85)
J. Gomez	Liverpool
H. Maguire	Leicester City
B. Chilwell	Leicester City
H. Winks	Tott. Hotspur (sub. N. Chalobah 90+1)
E. Dier	Tottenham Hotspur
R. Barkley	Chelsea (sub. K. Walker 76)
R. Sterling	Manchester City
H. Kane	Tottenham Hotspur
M. Rashford	Manchester United.

Result 3-2 Sterling 2, Rashford

ENGLAND INTERNATIONAL LINE-UPS AND STATISTICS 2018-2019

15th November 2018

v USA *Wembley*

J. Pickford Everton (sub. A. McCarthy 45)
T. Alexander-Arnold Liverpool
M. Keane Everton
L. Dunk Brighton & Hove Albion
B. Chilwell Leicester City (sub. E. Dier 57)
H. Winks Tott. Hotspur (sub. R. Loftus-Cheek 70)
F. Delph Manchester City
D. Alli Tott. Hotspur (sub. J. Henderson 57)
J. Sancho Borussia Dortmund
C. Wilson AFC Bournemouth (sub. M. Rashford 79)
J. Lingard Man. United (sub. W. Rooney 58)

Result 3-0 Lingard, Alexander-Arnold, King

18th November 2018

v CROATIA (NL) *Wembley*

J. Pickford Everton
K. Walker Manchester City
J. Gomez Liverpool
J. Stones Manchester City
B. Chilwell Leicester City
R. Barkley Chelsea (sub. D. Alli 63)
E. Dier Tottenham Hotspur
F. Delph Manchester City (sub. J. Lingard 73)
R. Sterling Manchester City
H. Kane Tottenham Hotspur
M. Rashford Man. United (sub. J. Sancho 73)

Result 2-1 Lingard, Kane

22nd March 2019

v CZECH REPUBLIC (ECQ) *Wembley*

J. Pickford Everton
K. Walker Manchester City
M. Keane Everton
H. Maguire Leicester City
B. Chilwell Leicester City
J. Henderson Liverpool
E. Dier Tott. Hotspur (sub. R. Barkley 17)
D. Alli Tottenham Hotspur (sub. D. Rice 63)
J. Sancho Borussia Dortmund
H. Kane Tottenham Hotspur
R. Sterling Man. City (sub. C. Hudson-Odoi 70)

Result 5-0 Sterling 3, Kane (pen), Kalas (og)

25th March 2019

v MONTENEGRO (ECQ) *Podgorica*

J. Pickford Everton
K. Walker Manchester City
M. Keane Everton
H. Maguire Leicester City
D. Rose Tottenham Hotspur
R. Barkley Chelsea (sub. J. Ward-Prowse 82)
D. Rice West Ham United
D. Alli Tott. Hotspur (sub. J. Henderson 64)
C. Hudson-Odoi Chelsea
H. Kane Tott. Hotspur (sub. C. Wilson 83)
R. Sterling Manchester City

Result 5-1 Keane, Barkley 2, Kane, Sterling

6th June 2019

v NETHERLANDS (NL) *Guimaraes*

J. Pickford Everton
K. Walker Manchester City
J. Stones Manchester City
H. Maguire Leicester City
B. Chilwell Leicester City
F. Delph Man. City (sub. J. Henderson 77)
D. Rice West Ham United (sub. D. Alli 105)
R. Barkley Chelsea
R. Sterling Manchester City
M. Rashford Manchester United (sub. H. Kane 45)
J. Sancho Bor. Dortmund (sub. J. Lingard 61)

Result 1-3 (aet) Rashford (pen)

9th June 2019

v SWIZERLAND (NL) *Guimaraes*

J. Pickford Everton
T. Alexander-Arnold Liverpool
J. Gomez Liverpool
H. Maguire Leicester City
D. Rose Tott. Hotspur (sub. K. Walker 70)
J. Lingard Man. United (sub. J. Sancho 105)
E. Dier Tottenham Hotspur
F. Delph Man. City (sub. R. Barkley 105)
D. Alli Tottenham Hotspur
R. Sterling Manchester City
H. Kane Tott. Hotspur (sub. C. Wilson 75)

Result 0-0 (aet)
England won 6-5 on penalties

Supporters' Guides and Tables books

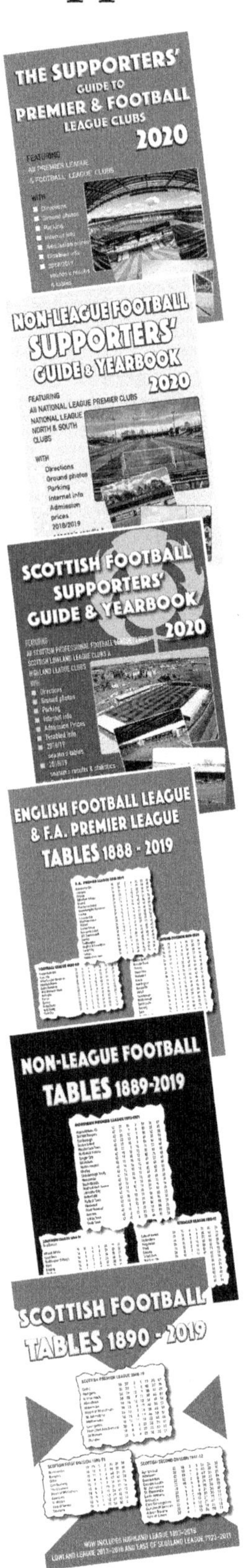

Our Supporters' Guide series has been published since 1982 and the new 2020 editions contain the 2018/2019 Season's results and tables, Directions, Photographs, Telephone numbers, Parking information, Admission details, Disabled information and much more.

Our Football Tables books are perfect companions to the Supporters' Guides and contain historical Football League, Non-League and Scottish final tables up to the end of the 2018/2019 season.

THE SUPPORTERS' GUIDE TO PREMIER & FOOTBALL LEAGUE CLUBS 2020

This 36th edition covers all 92 Premiership and Football League clubs. ***Price £9.99***

NON-LEAGUE SUPPORTERS' GUIDE AND YEARBOOK 2020

This 28th edition covers all 68 clubs in Step 1 & Step 2 of Non-League football – the Vanarama National League, National League North and National League South. ***Price £9.99***

SCOTTISH FOOTBALL SUPPORTERS' GUIDE AND YEARBOOK 2020

The 27th edition featuring all Scottish Professional Football League, Highland League and Lowland League clubs. ***Price £9.99***

ENGLISH FOOTBALL LEAGUE & F.A. PREMIER LEAGUE TABLES 1888-2019

The 22nd edition contains every Football League & F.A. Premier League final table plus play-off results and F.A. Cup and League Cup semi-final & final results. ***Price £9.99***

NON-LEAGUE FOOTBALL TABLES 1889-2019

The 18th edition contains final league tables and historical notes for the 3 Leagues operating at Steps 3 and 4 of the pyramid, the Northern Premier League, Southern League and Isthmian League. This edition also contains tables for the Gloucestershire Northern Senior League 1922-1968. ***Price £9.99***

SCOTTISH FOOTBALL TABLES 1890-2019

The 9th edition contains final league tables for all Scottish Professiona Football League, Scottish League, Scottish Premier League, Highlanc League and Lowland Football League seasons plus, for the first time the East of Scotland Football League. ***Price £9.99***

These books are available UK & Surface post free from –

Soccer Books Limited (Dept. SBL)
72 St. Peter's Avenue
Cleethorpes, DN35 8HU
United Kingdom